STRESS AND PSYCHIATRIC DISORDER

*The Proceedings of the Second Oxford Conference
of the Mental Health Research Fund*

EDITED BY

J. M. TANNER
M.D., D.Sc.

Secretary of Research Committee, Mental Health Research Fund

BLACKWELL
SCIENTIFIC PUBLICATIONS
OXFORD

© *Blackwell Scientific Publications Ltd.,* 1960

This book is copyright. It may not be reproduced by any means in whole or in part without permission. Application with regard to copyright should be addressed to the publishers.

Published simultaneously in the British Commonwealth of Nations by Blackwell Scientific Publications Ltd., 24-25 Broad Street, Oxford, England.

Published simultaneously in Canada by the Ryerson Press, Queen Street West, Toronto 2.

FIRST PUBLISHED 1960

PRINTED IN GREAT BRITAIN BY ADLARD & SON, LTD
BARTHOLOMEW PRESS, DORKING
AND BOUND BY THE KEMP HALL BINDERY, OXFORD

CONTENTS

MEMBERS OF CONFERENCE

Sir Geoffrey Vickers,
Chairman,
Research Committee,
Mental Health Research Fund,
London.

Dr Brian Ackner,
Consultant Psychiatrist,
The Maudsley Hospital,
London.

Dr. E. J. Anthony,*
Senior Lecturer in Psychiatry,
Institute of Psychiatry,
University of London.
* Present Address:—
Professor of Child Psychiatry,
Washington University,
St Louis.

Dr William Ross Ashby,
Director of Research,
Barnwood House,
Gloucester.

Dr John Bowlby,
Director,
Department for Children and Parents,
Tavistock Clinic,
London.

Dr G. M. Carstairs,
Assistant Director,
Medical Research Council Social
   Psychiatry Research Unit,
Institute of Psychiatry,
University of London.

Dr D. Russell Davis,
Reader in Medical Psychology,
University of Cambridge.

Dr Alick Elithorn,
Part-time member of Medical Research
Council Scientific Staff, National Hos-
pital for Nervous Diseases, London;
Consultant in Psychological Medicine,
Royal Free Hospital,
London.

Dr J. Fuller,
Staff Member,
R. B. Jackson Laboratory,
Bar Harbor, Maine.

Dr R.W. Gerard,
Professor Neurophysiology in Psychiatry and Physiology, Senior Research
Scientist, Mental Health Research Institute, University of Michigan.

Prof G. R. Hargreaves,
Professor of Psychiatry,
University of Leeds.

Lt-Col F. Gentry Harris,
Psychiatrist,
Walter Reed Army Institute of
   Research,
Washington, D.C.

Prof G. W. Harris,
Professor of Physiology,
Institute of Psychiatry,
University of London.

Dr. Denis Hill,
Physician for Psychological Medicine,
King's College Hospital,
London;
Senior Lecturer,
Institute of Psychiatry,
University of London.

Dr R. A. Hinde,
Curator, Field Station for the Study of
Animal Behaviour,
Department of Zoology, and
Fellow and Tutor of St John's College,
Cambridge.

Dr Hudson Hoagland,
Executive Director,
Worcester Foundation for Experimental
    Biology,
Shrewsbury, Massachusetts.

Prof Alexander Kennedy,
Professor of Psychological Medicine,
University of Edinburgh.

Dr John I. Lacey,
Chairman,
Department of Psychophysiology,
The Fels Research Institute for the
    Study of Human Development,
Yellow Springs,
Ohio.

Dr Marilyn C. Lee,
Professional Associate,
Behavioural Sciences Division,
U.S.A.F. Office of Scientific Research,
Brussels.

Dr Denis Leigh,
Consultant Psychiatrist,
The Maudsley Hospital,
London.

Sir Aubrey Lewis,
Professor of Psychiatry,
Institute of Psychiatry,
University of London.

Prof Howard S. Liddell,
Professor of Psychobiology,
Cornell University,
Ithaca.

Dr Erich Lindemann,
Professor of Psychiatry,
Harvard Medical School;
Psychiatrist-in-Chief,
Massachusetts General Hospital.

Prof W. M. Millar,
Professor of Mental Health,
University of Aberdeen.

Prof R. C. Oldfield,
Professor of Psychology,
University of Oxford.

Dr W. Linford Rees,
Physician in Charge,
Department of Psychological Medicine,
St. Bartholomew's Hospital, London;
Physician in Charge,
Bethlem Royal and Maudsley Hospitals,
London.

Dr Derek Richter,
Director,
Medical Research Council Neuro-
    psychiatric Research Unit,
Whitchurch Hospital,
Cardiff.

Prof T. Ferguson Rodger,
Professor of Psychological Medicine,
University of Glasgow.

Prof Martin Roth,
Professor of Psychological Medicine,
University of Durham.

Prof. Hans Selye,
Professor of Experimental Medicine
    and Surgery,
University of Montreal.

Dr J. D. Sutherland,
Director,
The Tavistock Clinic,
London.

Dr J. M. Tanner,
Secretary, Research Committee,
Mental Health Research Fund;
Senior Lecturer in Growth and
Development,
Institute of Child Health,
University of London.

Mr Eric L. Trist,
Psychologist,
Tavistock Institute of Human
Relations,
London.

Prof James Tyhurst,
Professor of Psychiatry,
University of British Columbia,
Vancouver.

Dr Grey Walter,
Director of Research,
Burden Neurological Institute,
Bristol.

Prof. Harold G. Wolff,
Anne Parrish Titzell
Professor of Medicine (Neurology),
Cornell University Medical College;
Attending Physician,
The New York Hospital,
New York.

Prof O. L. Zangwill,
Professor of Experimental Psychology,
University of Cambridge.

FOREWORD

This book records the proceedings of the Mental Health Research Fund four-day Conference on Stress and Psychiatric Disorder, held at Lincoln College, Oxford in July, 1958, which was attended by 36 leading psychiatrists, physiologists and animal experimentalists. It was the second international conference to be convened by the Fund, the first being that held at Magdalen College, Oxford in March, 1952, to discuss what ignorances principally hamper our understanding of mental illness: see *Prospects in Psychiatric Research* (Blackwell: Scientific Publications, Oxford, 21s. net). One of the objects of the Fund is to bring together leading scientists in this and other countries to examine problems bearing on mental health and mental illness: indeed, the pooling of knowledge thus effected is essential to the speeding of general advance on the whole psychiatric front.

The Mental Health Research Fund was brought into being in 1949 by a group of scientists, doctors and laymen who were concerned at the increasing gravity of human and sociological problems posed by an ever-growing volume of mental ill-health, the failure of existing knowledge to make any significant impression upon them, and the absence of adequate facilities and resources for psychiatric research. At the present time, the relevant facts are scarcely less serious though it is encouraging to note that the Medical Research Council has recently set up two advisory committees, one on clinical psychiatry and the other on the epidemiology of mental disorders, and that it is establishing two further research units in the psychiatric field, one concerned with genetics and the other with epidemiology: the directors of both these units are members of the Research Committee of the Fund.

But very much more remains to be done before it can be said that anything like an adequately organized and equipped research structure exists in this country. Half the total hospital beds are occupied by persons suffering from mental illness or mental deficiency; attendances at psychiatric out-patient departments number nearly a million a year; approximately one-third of the patients treated by general practitioners suffer from neurotic illness; some 80 million working days are lost annually in industry for reasons of neurosis; and 81,000 mental defectives are under supervision in the community. Our present scientific resources have failed to halt the steady rise in this private suffering and public burden. Research on an adequate scale is obviously needed, and it is clear that the stimulus of voluntary effort to promote it will be required for a very long time.

Thanks to generous grants by the Ford Foundation, the Leverhulme Trust Fund, the Dowager Countess Eleanor Peel Trust, the National Society for

Mentally Handicapped Children, and to testamentary bequests, contributions from industrial and other bodies and subscriptions from members of the general public, the Fund has been enabled to finance some 61 projects to the total of £120,000 (to December, 1959). The objects of the Fund include the establishment of research Fellowships and the support of specific lines of investigation by providing technical assistance or equipment. The projects supported cover a wide range of scientific disciplines: they include inquiries into the social and psychological aspects of mental illness and mental deficiency as well as into the anatomy and physiology of the brain. It is a measure of the success of the Fund that, since 1954, there has been a marked increase in the number, quality and variety of applications received Thus, although the sums committed annually have risen from £3,000 in 1954-5 to £36,000 in 1957-8, the stimulus to research has outrun the Fund's financial capacity to support it.

Hitherto, the Fund has been compelled, by the size of its resources, to confine itself to temporary grants. Such grants are of value in enabling experienced research workers to get temporary help for scientific projects and in increasing the number of posts open to those, usually in the earlier part of their careers, who wish to get research experience to establish themselves as productive research workers. Temporary posts, however, are only useful if they lead to and connect with a structure of permanent posts; otherwise, potential applicants for temporary posts are deterred from seeking them by the knowledge that they will lead nowhere. The Fund has these considerations prominently in mind in connection with its future policy.

The task of organizing the Conference fell on the Research Committee of the Fund, and particularly its Chairman, Sir Geoffrey Vickers, and its Secretary, Dr. J. M. Tanner. Dr. Tanner also undertook the major task of editing the shorthand transcript of this book. Our sincere thanks are due to them; to the President of Lincoln College for permission to hold the Conference there; to the Bursar and his staff for the excellent arrangements they made; and to two members of the staff of the Fund, Mrs. Susan Giles and Miss Claudette Rampling, who had the very arduous task of collecting and checking the several manuscripts and preparing the book for Press.

I. T. Henderson,
Chairman, Mental Health Research Fund.

Maurice Craig House,
39 Queen Anne Street,
London, W.1.

January, 1960.

CHAPTER 1

INTRODUCTION TO CONFERENCE

THE CONCEPT OF STRESS IN RELATION TO THE DISORGANIZATION OF HUMAN BEHAVIOUR

SIR GEOFFREY VICKERS

Mental Health Research Fund, London

The object of this Conference is to clarify the concepts of 'stress' and 'stressor' as used in psychiatry and to explore the relationship of these concepts to the different phenomena for which the same terms are used by students of animal behaviour on the one hand and by physiologists on the other.

At first sight it seems clear that the phenomena that the psychiatrist studies are more easily comparable with those which concern the student of animal behaviour than with those which confront the physiologist. This is because both the animal experimenter and the animal ethologist, like the psychiatrist, start from an observed correlation between a 'situation' and a 'disorganization of behaviour'. Disorganization can take many forms: the unbearably frustrated man may break down into rage or tears or lethargy; he may begin to act at random or to adopt irrelevant behaviour, or to stop acting at all. So, within his compass, may the frustrated rat behave, and these differences in form of breakdown may be interesting as indices of temperament — but all serve equally well as indices of disorganization.

So the first question as I see it is: how do we recognize this characteristic disorganization despite its variety of form? Shall we take as our index the fact that the behaviour under review has become non-adaptive, inept to the situation that has provoked it? That will not quite do, because neurosis can be protective in man and perhaps also in animals. In any case, is it really adaptive for a man in a bewitched cockpit or a rat in a bewitched maze to go on ringing the changes on responses that have become irrelevant? I recall a question asked by a psychiatrist at a previous Conference of this Fund when some colleague had described a particularly devilish form of animal frustration. What, he asked, would be a non-neurotic reaction to a situation of that kind? I do not recall that he received any convincing reply.

It seems that what we call disorganization may be, perhaps always is, a form of defensive reorganization, and I would guess that Professor Lindemann may have a good word to say for the protective value of some kinds of psychological stress response.

But of course this protection is bought at a cost. Field-Marshal Lord Wavell, in some famous lectures on his profession, said that stupidity in generals should never excite surprise, because generals were selected from the extremely small class of human beings who were tough enough to be generals at all. The essential qualification was not that they should be extremely clever or sensitive, but that they should continue to function, even if not particularly well, in situations in which more sensitive or less stable organisms would have stopped functioning altogether.

The criteria for determining disorganization seem to imply the passing of some threshold beyond which external relations can no longer be handled at the previous level. This is either because internal coherence has been lost or because internal coherence has only been preserved at the cost of some 'withdrawal'. These may be two extremely different states.

Turning to the other side, if pressed to define the situations that provoke disorganization, both the psychiatrist and the student of animal behaviour could be driven to some tentative formulations. This is particularly true of the animal experimentalists who design the situations they are studying and who must, therefore, have some criteria for designing them. Once again the descriptions they give have curious imprecision.

Pavlov, I believe, used four main types: progressive increase in intensity of the signals to which the animal is conditioned; progressive increase in the delay between the signal and the satisfaction; confusion by the introduction of conflicting signals; and interference with the physical condition. If you leave out the last and divide the third into doubt, where the signals are ambiguous, conflict where they are inconsistent and frustration, where the signal is not followed by its accustomed sequel, you still have not covered all the situations suggested by Professor Liddell's work, which includes several other situations such as loneliness, monotony and self-imposed restraint, which required categories of their own.

So this is a very wide field of characteristic situations, and it is curious that they can most readily be described by words drawn from the subjective vocabulary of human kind: apprehension, suspense, doubt, conflict or frustration. I think psychiatrists would agree that these categories also cover most of the situations that they recognize as provocative of stress in man, although, of course, they are too vague so far to be very much use. At all events this suggests fairly clearly that these situations, which we know through introspection, reflect conditions of neural excitement which are not confined to conscious states or to nervous systems as complex as our own.

The other curious enigma is that most, and possibly all, of them require for their convenient description the concept of *expectation*, whether it be the hateful expectation which can neither be accepted nor avoided, the pleasurable expectation which is intolerably deferred, the confusion of expectation which produces confused response, or the sheer absence of expectation which removes the basis for action. The fact that this concept of expectation — again a rather imprecise concept — crops up so often in the design of animal experiments shows that here too we are up against something which must be describable in terms of neural activity not related to conscious human states.

It is at that point, I suggest, that the psychiatrist and the student of animal behaviour can legitimately turn to the physiologist, including the physiologist in themselves, for help. The organism is not functioning the way it was; what is the nature of this change of function and how and why has it occurred? These seem questions which it is very proper to put to a specialist in organic function. Until recently I think a physiologist would not have had very much to say to them. He could supply an impressive model of the internal relations of the organism; he could describe the homeostatic mechanisms that neutralize the impact of external variables such as heat or cold. He could describe the course of the defensive activities as they are overcome by forces too strong for the defences, forces which, in Professor Selye's classic formulation, he knows as stressors. He could describe the adaptive changes that enable the organism in an emergency to hold its own for a while against overwhelming forces — the sort of changes through which a man chased by a bull can mobilize for a few minutes a quite surprising amount of energy. But why an approaching bull should function as a stressor no less than a change of temperature, and still more why the hope of winning an Olympic mile should function as a stressor no less than an approaching bull, are questions which the physiologist is less prepared to answer. Nor is it clear, certainly not to me, that the collapse of the runner after he has jumped a gate or burst a tape has very much in common with the kind of collapse studied by the psychiatrist or the student of animal behaviour.

So the stressful situation which concerns the psychiatrist and, therefore, which ultimately concerns the physiologist, is not given by events but by the organisms' interpretation of events in relation to itself. This, in turn, is a function of the way in which its individual personality is organized, and any conceptual model of that must include the organization of experience.

We have several conceptual models of organization. There is the physiological model, which until recently had not very much to say about the organization of experience. There is the body of psychological concepts dealing with perception and learning theory, and there is the multi-dimensional model implicit in psychodynamic theory. All of these deal with systems obtained by abstracting different sets of variables from this baffling observable entity — man. A better integration of these models is an urgent need which we hope this Conference will advance, and a great deal of what is happening currently is most excitingly advancing this integration, far more than certainly a layman like myself can summarize. The anatomist finds in the nervous system paths by which past experience can modify the sensory input before it gets to the association areas — a rather sinister form of feedback, as it seems to me. The pharmacologist has an increasing battery of drugs of known constitution which can directly modify psychological states.

Observations by EEG begin to give a physiological measure of some differences of human type and perhaps of difference of personal integration and have suggested to Dr Grey Walter a physiological theory of learning. Both psychiatrists and animal experimentalists are adding to the correlations which relate physiological and biochemical changes to psychological changes at the threshold of breakdown. Animal experimentalists have demonstrated the genetic basis for differential immunity and vulnerability to stress in animals. Animal ethologists have provided a set of concepts which seem to me to have a curious interest in that both physiologists and psychoanalysts can use them without either a sense of unreality or a sense of sin, and that is a very welcome widening of our common universe of discourse.

Then there is the interesting and I think very important increase in the development of language and concepts apt to describe open systems generally. The concept of stability, for instance, that Dr Ross Ashby has done so much to generalize, seems to me to be equally applicable to systems studied by the physiologist, the psychologist or the sociologist. The same concept applies equally to those much more numerous cases in which the governing controls of the system are not fixed but change with time, such as the pattern of growth and maturation or, for that matter, the pattern of a changing cultural norm. Homeostasis is a special case of a much wider process that Professor Waddington recently christened homeorhesis.

There is one idea in all these fields which may be of central importance to the theme of this Conference, and that is the idea of matching with a pattern. It is abundantly clear that the raw material of experience is not the whole of the 'blooming, buzzing confusion' but a selection of the regularities which we detect. These in turn provide categories for classifying future experience. Conditioning and probably much more beside, depends on recognizing regular relations between recurrent events in the categories thus distinguished. Even judgments of values, those most refined of tropisms, are also linked to situations recognized by their correspondence with a pattern, however complex. If I say that A has given me a fair deal, I must first have selected a number of aspects of my relations with A and then classified them as a deal, rather than say a battle, and then applied the standards of 'fair deal' rather than 'fair fight'. I must then observe that they match, and the process that arrives at the judgment of 'fair' is equally a matching process, like the process which arrives at the judgment of 'deal' and I see no reason why it should not be carried out in the same code.

So pattern governs throughout, and though the mind may boggle at the thought of a black box no bigger than our heads that can group and re-group and handle shifting configurations of symbols so complex and plastic and yet so enduring, we boggle at the complexity rather than the principle. So perhaps it is not so surprising that this thing that we vaguely call 'expectation' should figure so largely in the organization and disorganization of personality, because clearly what we know as expectation is only the exposed part of an iceberg that floats very low in the water.

In pursuing, maintaining and elaborating the external relations by which we live and die, we are clearly guided by symbolic representations of what is happening and of what 'ought' to be happening. I think we need a model of this process to understand the nature and the noxious operation of stress. Contrariwise, in looking for a model to explain the noxious working of stress, we may well contribute to our understanding of controlled behaviour, because obviously organization and disorganization are opposite sides of the same penny.

The fact that meaning derives from relationship to the familiar is evident from the fact that when we have not got a templet from experience we have to invent one. That is exemplified at an entirely different level by another conceptual model with which I happen to be more familiar and which I do not think is as remote from our subject as may first appear. In the practical affairs of life we assume that conduct is controlled to a very important degree by structures of expectation, and the implications of this have been worked out both in theory and practice to a high degree of refinement in the field of administration. Nobody today would try to run a Government depart-ment or a university or a business without maintaining and continually comparing two running representations of the future. One is a representation of what is happening, projected into the future to give what is going to happen next, and the other is a representation of the course of events that we want to bring about or prevent; call one the actual and the other the standard, the one the 'is' and the other the 'ought to be'. The comparison of these two yields a stream of mismatch signals on which we act. The building contractor plots on charts against time the planned course of many interdependent operations, and then, as work proceeds, he plots what is actually achieved and projects that also into the future. The divergence of those two lines on the chart provides the signal for reflection and action, first to bring the 'is' into line with the 'ought to be' and, if that cannot be done, to bring the 'ought to be' into line with the 'is' so as to provide a workable control. These controls that are used in administration are representations of relationships that we seek to maintain or alter or escape. Some relationships are between the organization and its environment, and some are relationships within the organization itself. In either case the control may be negative or positive, directed either to bringing back the state continually to an optimum position, or to preventing it from straying beyond some critical threshold. Even in this down-to-earth world in which I am more accustomed to move, the 'actual' is a highly artificial construction; in the first place it is hypothetical — our information about what is happening is never complete, exact or direct. It is also selective, because we can only attend to a few aspects of it at a time. It is also represented in a code, be it in writing or figures or graphically, which limits and distorts what can be represented, and that is necessarily also the code in which you represent the 'standard', otherwise you could not compare them. Finally, it has an inescapable time base. In all of these things I think it closely parallels the working of the individual mind.

These controls, like those that control us personally, do not always give clear or correct or adequate guidance. They apply only to those aspects of experience to which we have chosen to attend. We may have chosen the wrong variables for attention, or the signals may be ambiguous or, being clear, experience may supply no apt response; or the responses that have worked in the past may let us down. But the most inescapable feature of these responses is their conflict. This is a feature of practical life, as we all know. Any projected action is relevant not only to the purposive sequence in which it arises, but to others also, and if it is apt for some, it is inept for others; whatever doors it will open, others it will shut. In business, short-term profit, long-term stability, internal coherence, public relations — each of these disparate standards, when compared with an appropriate selection from the actual, maintains its own stream of warning and advice, and these are no more consistent in business than in private life. Moreover their inconsistency is inescapable. The highly organized business, like the highly organized personality, necessarily generates more inconsistency in its governing expectations than one less highly organized. This may perhaps account for the fact that the stress of war produces relatively so little civilian neurosis, life in wartime being harder but also simpler.

Apart from the inadequacies just described, the controls of business are partial and intermittent, because either the actual or the intended may not be accessible. Like the fog-bound navigator we may know where we ought to be but have no means of knowing where we are. Or like the climber following an unfamiliar route, we may see where we are but have no assurance that it is where we ought to be. Nor can experience be guaranteed to remedy either case, because the results of our action may return for judgment so long after the event and mixed with so many other variables that they may supply neither validation of the past nor guidance for the future.

In the board room, then, stress is associated with doubt and conflict of clearly definable kinds. We may have to live for years with deafening streams of mismatch signals, either because we can devise no suitable response or, much more often, because any response we made would elicit even more violent protest in another context. Alternatively we may have to live in an eerie silence because either the actual or the standard is not registering in the appropriate code. I assure you that either of those states can produce disorganization or perhaps protective reorganization which is very suggestive of the forms that are familiar to the psychiatrist and to the animal experimentalist.

This digression into what seems rather a remote field seems to be significant for three reasons. First, it does exemplify clearly the nature and limitations of that control by matching which we meet at all levels. It seems to me that even the simplest innate response involves selecting something from the stream of experience and matching it with a pattern. Even that famous herring gull chick does not respond to a red patch; it responds to the similarity between an observed red patch, which is a complicated abstraction, and the standard red patch with which it is equipped. The similarity may not be absolute but falls within limits of tolerance which are also built in. Of course learned responses can be built around cues much more extensive in space and time and which are also distilled from experience. It seems, then, that this process of matching with a pattern is inherent in the control of behaviour from the simplest response up to the most sophisticated act of cognition, because all cognition is recognition. Moreover these patterns which the brain can record are patterns in time as well as in space. An instrument which can record change with time can represent the hypothetical future as well as the past.

Secondly, I think the model is useful in its representation of conflict as endemic and necessarily increasing with the complexity of organization. By complexity of organization I mean not increase in size or increase in power and variety of responses available, or even increase in subdivision of function. I mean rather increase in the number and diversity of the objectives to be sought and the thresholds to be avoided, in other words, in the norms which the system is set simultaneously to seek and the limits which it is set simultaneously to avoid. That is the dimension along which it seems to me both organism and organization tend to develop and along which they tend to fall back, whenever they set themselves a task of reconciliation which proves to be too much for their powers.

Finally, I think the example is useful in stressing a new dimension in which higher organisms, no less than organizations are adaptable. Most biological work treats as given the acceptable and unacceptable states which act as governors, positive and negative, of a system's behaviour. In so far as this is so the only scope for adaptation within the individual life span is the development of the responses and the skills which serve those needs. But at higher levels, conspicuously at the level of human life, the individual's wants and needs, no less than his responses and skills, grow and multiply within the life span. An increasing number of different but mutually exclusive possibilities compete for realization within the framework of the biologically given. We take a hand in the setting of our own systems; and this is perhaps the point at which our common conceptual model needs to be enlarged if it is to link physiological with psychological observation. The biologist is already at grips with the code built into the molecular structure of the gene. But the psychologist, who works within a very different time span, needs more than that; he needs a model not merely of the programme of the organism from birth to death, but of its self-programming capacity and its self-programming propensity, a model that can represent our goal-setting as well as our goal-seeking. Though these two activities of goal-setting and goal-seeking are so intimately related that they cannot be considered separately, they are also I think so distinct that they cannot usefully be simplified, as is often done, by simply resolving one into the other.

Finally, let me conclude by reminding myself and you that a model of conflict does not necessarily tell us anything at all about pathological stress. Conflict is endemic; breakdown is still, happily, relatively exceptional. We need not — and therefore must not — assume that conflict in itself is noxious. If the threshold is quantitative, it is also relative, for it must certainly depend both on the amount of stress and on the resistance, or perhaps we should call it the immunity, of the organism affected. We need to understand both the noxious nature of a given stress in relation to the organization of a given organism and the vulnerability of a given organism to a particular form of stress. That of course, involves an elaboration of the conceptual model far ahead of anything on which I have yet touched.

CHAPTER 2

DISORGANIZATION OF BEHAVIOUR IN MAN

PSYCHO-SOCIAL FACTORS AS STRESSOR AGENTS

Erich Lindemann

Department of Psychiatry, Harvard University Medical School

I use the word anticipation where Sir Geoffrey Vickers speaks about expectation, and I agree that the relating of anticipation and memory into meaningful programming seems indeed to be an essential function of the organism. Not only is this more and more substantiated by neurophysiological observations in the fied of perception and by observations on action programming, but it is now more and more clearly circumscribed in terms of various aspects of the organization of social functioning.

This may be illustrated by some observations concerning a particular form of stress response, namely bereavement. Bereavement constitutes the reactions to a special type of social stress, meaning the cessation of interaction with another emotionally relevant person (Lindemann, 1944, 1950, 1957). Here we like to distinguish adaptive and mal-adaptive responses. This cessation of interaction leads regularly to a sequence of events in the physiological system (such as weeping, autonomic, respiratory or digestive changes) in the psychological system and in the social system.

In the psychological system we find a rather interesting sequence of events. The perceptual field becomes reorganized in such a way that the image of the deceased becomes the centre, to the disadvantage of other contents. There are dramatic intensifications of the clarity and vividness of the image, which at times takes on an hallucinatory quality. The habitual action patterns of the griever are changed so that the sequence of activities which would normally go on throughout the day is replaced by stereotyped small amounts of activity, psycho-motor restlessness and agitation. It appears that many partial action programmes for each day which have been executed regularly were conditioned to the presence of a social alter ego with whom this programme was executed in patterned social interaction.

In successful grieving there ensues a process which Freud has called 'mourning work'. An essential aspect of this effort is a review of past interaction events in such a way that the question can be raised 'what will happen now?' It is possible to do this work in small manageable quantities relating to specific situations. It can also be done in a global manner — 'was this person not wonderful to me always?' — in referring to large areas of patterns of relatedness rather than to concrete specific interaction. If that happens the process of mourning work does not seem to succeed.

Almost all severely bereaved persons are impaired in their functioning for a period often lasting about six weeks. However, this reaction is self-limiting and leads on to reorganization of conscious preoccupations, to recession of the autonomic disturbance and to a redistribution of interaction patterns within the social orbit. Under pathological circumstances this does not take place properly, and then we may find psychosomatic disorders, for example, ulcerative colitis. There may also be disorders in the area of mood disturbances, and lasting impairment of social interaction. In each of these conditions of marked grief the mourning process fails to take place. Indeed, it appears that emergency measures are taken by the grieving person to avoid its painful implications.

The most striking of these is selective forgetting. The image of the deceased disappears from consciousness and cannot be recalled even with effort, or returns only in dream material and will only be recalled with great reluctance and great difficulty during waking hours. Concurrently with this amnesia traits of the deceased person's behaviour appear in the survivor. We speak of 'morbid identification with the deceased' and consider it as a maladaptive pattern of response to the stress of losing an emotionally relevant other person.

To illustrate: A thirty-two year old woman who lost her husband from lupus erythematosus came three weeks afterwards to us convinced that she now had lupus erythematosus. Expecting and anticipating this illness, she had produced infections of the outer lips and brought about a semblance on her own face of the facial disease she had witnessed in her husband.

Well-adaptive patterns of grief lead to a reorganization of the social system of the survivor. This process is also facilitated by social custom. Societies have mourning rites of various kinds to fit in with the psychological and perhaps the physiological operations involved in the mourning process. Certain societies show evidence of rather maladaptive ceremonials similar to the pathological defences of the individual. Furthermore, certain societies, for instance American contemporary society, show a family and kinship organization which makes a severe mourning reaction particularly likely. The pattern of the 'isolated conjugal unit', in contrast to the wide and elaborate kinship systems of the Italian ethnic group, for instance, is likely to contribute to the intensity and frequency of severe maladaptive reactions.

The consideration of social structures with respect to their facilitating or impeding effects on problem-solving or stress-meeting behaviour is of some interest. Spiegel (1959) and Kluckhohn (1958) for example, have been comparing the reactions of Italian and Irish families, particularly as to the way in which their kinship organizations act as a help or hindrance for problem solving not only in bereavement but in the difficulties engendered by the acculturation process. In addition to the formal organization of the family, they have considered the way in which the culturally transmitted codes of conduct and goals are shared by the members of society and determine what is permissible conduct and what is demanded conduct within the society. Seen in this context many of the stress responses labelled neurotic or psychosomatic reactions, which might previously have been viewed as personal psychological failure of mastery of a problem, turn out to be 'typically Irish' ways of solving problems related to mother/child relations, in contrast, for example, to Italian or other ethnic patterns. The role distribution within the family as well as the kinship system becomes a relevant factor in determining the likelihood of solving certain aspects of social stress.

We have also become interested in a number of studies relating observations concerning bereavement to certain aspects of role transition. The characteristic challenge which must be met at the time of bereavement requires the abandoning of a position within the social orbit (with a certain programme related to the expectation of others and of oneself) and the replacing of it with a new programme. The need for more or less sudden reprogramming as part of a role transition necessarily arises at certain life stages within the individual life cycle. We have studied the stress responses in certain children seen at the time of entrance into kindergarten and again at the time of leaving school for a profession. We have considered these occasions of role transition as opportunities for discerning patterns of problem solving or of failure to master the stress involved. Under these circumstances one can distinguish several patterns in which the anticipation of future roles is matched with past roles. Home-sickness is a good example of a modified form of a bereaved state.

We also find within this group of children the evolution of patterns of social interaction which appear rather enduring throughout the subsequent school career. One such pattern in which we have been interested is the pattern of a dyad relationship. A child will choose one other child as an obligatory companion through whom is mediated access to other people and a large segment of the role functions which the child exercises.

We have followed one group of such children for six years, another group for five, and we find that these particular dyad relationships are of great endurance. This is important in connection with the observation that the most severe psychosomatic forms of bereavement which we encountered occurred in individuals for whom the deceased constituted the one significant person in the social orbit, a person who mediated most of the satisfactions and provided the opportunity for a variety of role functions which were impossible without him.

In summary, I have tried to start off this discussion by concrete illustrations in the nature of responses to a special form of social stress, namely, bereavement. This is a stressful situation brought about by the cessation of interaction with an emotionally relevant other person. It leads to patterns of response with physiological, psychological and social facets. The response may be well-adaptive and lead to an adequate solution of the problem and indeed to an improvement of the overall condition of the responding person. It may also be maladaptive leading to disorganization, failure to resolve the problem and indeed to disease. Such social stress presents a hazardous situation to a plurality of people who will respond differently dependent on physiological, psychological and particularly on social system determinants. The reorganization of the social system is an essential part of the problem solving process. The stressful situation becomes a 'crisis' for many individuals in so far as it necessitates intra-individual and external reorganizations which do not belong to the 'arsenal' of habitual adjustive responses.

STRESSORS AS A CAUSE OF DISEASE IN MAN

Harold G. Wolff

Department of Medicine, New York Hospital

Although long used in common language, the word 'stress' has been given by physicists a precise definition as applied to the mechanics of non-living systems. Obviously the resemblance to the situation in living systems is remote, yet figuratively the concept is useful. I have used the word in human biology to indicate that state within a living creature which results from the interaction of the organism with noxious stimuli or circumstances. Thus, it is a dynamic state within an organism; it is not stimulus, assault, load symbol, burden, or any aspect of environment; internal, external, social or otherwise.[1]

Noxious stimuli or circumstances may be divided, as regards stress, into two extreme categories with myriad intermediate mixed forms resulting in a continuum. A contrast between extremes is as follows.

Those in the first category may be referred to as *unconditional*, and may be said to act directly, damaging and distorting structure and function. Such stimulation would result from relatively strong mechanical, thermal, electrical and corrosive chemical agents. The ensuing protective or adaptive reactions are inborn or early acquired, are less individual, more stock-bound, more predictable and stable, less dependent upon individual past experience and the setting in which stimulation takes place, with a relatively close relationship in time between stimulus and response. Also, the bodily responses are more or less appropriate in kind though commonly inappropriate in amount. Indeed such reactions to a noxious stimulus may be more destructive than the direct effects of the stimulus. They may evoke no behavioural, attitudinal or other psychological defences and mood changes may be absent. Thus, in man, after mid thoracic spinal transection, noxious stimulation of the bladder may raise the blood pressure, cause local vasomotor and pilomotor changes without inducing psychological reactions. Therefore, although the responses involve the integrated action of the nervous system, the patterns are usually of a primitive type.

Stimuli in the second category may be referred to as *conditional* and may

---

[1] For other uses of the word 'stress' see page 31.

be said to act indirectly. They usually have little or no direct noxious effect in themselves and assume significance only because of their capacity to act as signals or symbols. The nature of the adaptive reactions they evoke is dependent entirely on individual past experience and to some degree upon the stock. They are less predictable and less stable, readily modified by the setting in which stimulation occurs, and there is very commonly no close relationship in time between stimulus and response. Behavioural, attitudinal and other psychological defences and mood disturbances are the rule. When evoked the bodily responses are only to a very limited degree appropriate in kind and usually inappropriate in amount. They may however, be long sustained and extremely destructive. These complex reactions during stress always involve the central nervous system and especially the highest integrative functions. The meaning of the stimuli for the individual makes them assume the nature of the threats.

Few stimuli or circumstances involving symbols have universal value. They assume significance only in terms of the perception of the individual exposed to them. Furthermore, perception is of many kinds and usually only to a limited degree does it implicate consciousness. Thus, gravely threatening symbols to a given individual may be meaningless to the neutral observer. Yet equipped with facts of the individual's past, such an observer may make reasonably correct predictions as to the likelihood of a defined set of circumstances being noxious or threatening.

Nature of Threat for Man

Central to the problem of stress for man is his special sensitivity to his place in the eyes of other men. Man is a tribal creature with a long period of development, and depends for his very existence on the aid, support and encouragement of other men. Events having to do with his place in his society take on major significance and he is often at his best when his own ends are totally subordinate to the common end, or to the 'Glory of God'. Inversely when frustrated in such efforts, or rejected by his group, serious aberrations and death may ensue. He is threatened when growth, development, and fulfilment of individual proclivities are blocked, and even when his aesthetic needs and creative potential are not sated, as well as by jeopardy to survival of self and kin and to opportunities for procreation. Further the existence of his lively appetite for challenge, exploration and adventure is likely to lead to frustration and enhanced vulnerability.

Though challenge for man is essential and some threat desirable if not necessary for proper human development, threats to the stability of initmate human relations, especially during the dependent years, and threats that wipe out hope and faith in man are grave in their significance. Stress for him, therefore, is largely linked with the reaction to noxious symbols, and especially those involving threatening human relations.

Particular mention should be made of stimuli stemming from sudden and violent alterations in environment that in themselves have little direct noxious effect, but because they alter basic and established relations between the creature and his environment, engender stress and often evoke major reactions inappropriate in kind and amount. I have in mind the kind of situation exhibited by some American Indian tribes taken from their plains and put into reservations within a few miles' distance, living in essentially the same physical environment, but in a setting of social disorganization. There was an appalling increase in the mortality from tuberculosis. There was a violent and sudden change which altered established relationships, whereas light, food, sun, air, hygienic circumstances and clothing remained ostensibly unaltered.

Also worthy of special mention, since they engender stress, are those stimuli that although non-noxious in themselves, are repetitious non-challenging or monotonous. On the other hand, there is that category of excessive stimulation especially relevant to those persons whose pursuit of adventure and excitement, and whose appetite for challenge, exceed their capacities.

Patterns of Response to Destructive and Painful Stimulation and to Circumstances Perceived as Threatening

Reactions evoked during circumstances perceived as threatening are quite different when the threat has one significance rather than another. For example, opposite patterns of reaction occur in the human stomach when, on the one hand, circumstances are perceived as terrifying, or on the other, when a threat provokes aggressive action and violent anger. Two extremes are readily recognizable: a response characterized by overactivity and one by underactivity. Each is clearly linked with definable features of behaviour, attitudes and feelings.

Most people have a proclivity for using one pattern of reaction to threat rather than others, for example, reactions involving stomach, rather than the large bowel. They may react to threats in this one way for many years, using other patterns only now and then. Several members of one family often show similar patterns. However, even though a given person when confronted by a similar situation usually reacts in the same way, when a new significance is attached to the situation, new reactions appear. In the course of a lifetime several different patterns may be evoked in people who are threatened by numerous circumstances or who only transiently achieve a suitable adaptation.

Some persons, because of inborn or early acquired differences, feel threatened by circumstances which are not at all alarming to most people. In such cases ostensibly benign circumstances may evoke inappropriate responses.

Faulty Adaptation and the Use of Supportive Measures

When a person's goals are defined and progress toward their achievement is satisfactory — without excessive conflict, postponement, or deprivation — the individual may be said to be in a phase of adequate adaptation. But when for some reason, the individual feels himself to be seriously threatened and blocked in the pursuit or the fulfilment of his goals, he is said to be in a non-adapted phase. A conspicuous feature of this extremely precarious phase is an uneasy feeling – usually ill-defined – which is best described as anxiety. The person may also be aware that his thinking is not clear.

Since an individual does not necessarily recognize all of his goals, and since the goals themselves are often in conflict and anxiety is at least transiently experienced by everyone, protective, defensive, and compensatory reactions help an individual both to avoid and meet this non-adaptive phase, by carrying him through periods of great environmental demands.

A multitude of such protective devices may be set up even in the absence of awareness of anxiety. Unacceptable facts, situations, or conflicts may be repressed, forgotten, denied, misrepresented, pretended to be other than they are, made light of, joked or clowned about. Excessive attention and show of affection may be demanded. The pursuit of popularity may be overdone. Blame may be fixed on something outside oneself. Alibis and excuses may be used. A substitute for the insoluble conflict or circumstance may be attacked, overcome, resolved, or vicarious 'success' achieved where perfectionism, or tireless application can achieve results. A detached, impersonal, aloof, remote attitude may be assumed. The dilemma may be 'depersonalized', or the individual may withdraw from the struggle and become apathetic. He may substitute a pattern of behaviour suitable for one purpose to meet a situation in which it is ineffective. A socially acceptable emotion may be substituted for one that is frowned on — anxious solicitude for hatred, for example. The person may even court defeat. These and other defensive devices and combinations once established, maintained, and elabrated in a socially acceptable way, may become permanent components of personality. Even those ominous reactions that characterize the behaviour of people with schizophrenia, depersonalization, or feeling and acting as though the catastrophe one faces is of no personal significance — even these can be used transiently as protective measures.

Should the load become too great, however, or the frustration too prolonged or profound, or should time fail to resolve the dilemma, defences may break down, allowing an uneasy, tense, anxious mood to emerge. More primitive devices may then be called forth to supplement the first defences. Behaviour patterns involving alimentation or those with urinary, sexual, respiratory, cardiovascular, glandular, and vasomotor activity are common. These substitutions or displaced patterns can function excessively and for long periods while the subject is otherwise relatively effective and free of the costly feelings of anxiety, tension, hostility and depression. Were it not for the untoward effect on the bodily tissues themselves, such adaptive arrangements might go on indefinitely. Occasionally, they do persist without serious consequences. But often, bodily illness results.

The Problem of Disease

Claude Bernard was among the first to see disease as the outcome of attempts at adaptation — attempts which though appropriate in kind, are faulty in amount. Since the defensive response in its intensity can be more destructive than the original assault, an individual may be gravely damaged through the magnitude of his defensive reactions. For instance, the presence of micro-organisms in the lung calls forth cellular and humoral reactions that counter invasion, and do so effectively. Yet their magnitude may lead to congestion of the lungs and to pneumonia. This adaptive response becomes especially ominous for the individual when tissue is already involved in a longstanding over-reaction as in chronic lung disease.

Because of the unity of mind and body, man reacts adaptively or defensively not only to damaging microbial forces, but to threats and symbols of danger. Circumstances perceived as threatening may evoke inappropriately primitive metabolic or reproductive patterns that ordinarily serve to maintain the body and the stock. Since certain bodily and behaviour patterns are called upon to attain goals that can never be attained through their use, such inappropriate reactions are indefinitely protracted. The tissues involved are thus pressed beyond their limits. In other words, devices that ordinarily serve to protect the body may destroy tissue. The evidence for this is now abundant.

Over the years in my laboratory one organ or system of organs after the other has been studied in people living in the context of their homes and work environment. When an individual is placed in a setting which he perceives as a threat of a certain type, the mucous membrane lining of his stomach becomes intensely engorged, its acid secretion greatly accelerated, and its rhythmic contractions augmented. This is the stomach pattern of a man preparing to eat a meal. Under circumstances that call for entirely different reactions of aggression or striking in anger, the individual in-

3

appropriately evokes an eating pattern. Similarly, the crying-out anger pattern, with hunger — one of the earliest to appear in infancy — may reassert itself in later life during periods of deprivation or repression of longings for emotional support. Since this displacement behaviour seen in the eating patterns cannot satisfy such longings, the gastric activity is excessively prolonged and the lining of the stomach may digest itself. Peptic ulceration may ensue.

In studies of the large bowel it has been observed that in those who perceive themselves as threatened in a given way, quantitites of blood engorge the mucous membranes and motility and secretion are augmented. This is the pattern of ejection — one that could be used in ridding the organism of materials inadvertently taken in — yet it is used inappropriately to help the man rid himself of an unattractive human problem that cannot be dealt with in this way. Abnormal secretions and the by-products of breakdown may then destroy the lining of the bowel, resulting in ulcerative colitis.

Studies of the mucous membranes of the nose, upper airways and lungs have shown that circumstances which the individual perceives as threatening may result in engorgements of the mucosae, increase in secretions of mucous and protective cells and contraction of smooth muscle of the airways, and even spasm of skeletal muscle. The eyes may tear and close. This is the pattern properly evoked by dangerous gases, fumes, dust and micro-organisms, and it serves well to shut out, neutralize, and wash away. Yet it is also used by some people in dealing with an offensive man-to-man situation. Because of excessive and inappropriate use, the reaction may dispose to chronic infection, chronic obstructive disease, and asthma. Alterations in the chemical make-up of the secretions within the lungs may end in tuberculosis by affording an opportunity for organisms to reproduce when otherwise they would die.

Many skin disorders arise under threatening circumstances because of inappropriate responses of the blood vessels and unusual secretions in the skin. Under like conditions, the kidney may be damaged because it gets too little blood, with great outpouring or retention of water and salt. So also the heart and blood vessels of the body may overwork and contract excessively as though the individual were stopping a mortal hemorrhage, or facing a crisis of fight or flight — when, as a matter of fact, he may be sitting inertly in his office chair.

No organ or part of the body is spared these inappropriate responses so suggestive of the displacement behaviour patterns of the rat and the gull. Yet not all reactions involving man's highly developed nervous system, that end as disease are 'displacement' patterns. A conspicuous example is the migraine headache which results from the painful dilatation of the blood vessels of the head and which often occurs as a sequel of a long period of alertness or extraordinary effort. One could easily add a host of other depletion, exhaustion, and collapse phenomena that follow excessive striving.

Since displacement patterns and other such inappropriate responses are integrated by the brain, one naturally wonders whether this organ itself, in integrating highest level adaptive responses, may be damaged as a consequence of improper interaction between organism and environment, more particularly interaction between one human creature and others. There is much to indicate that this is so.

In men, and in some laboratory animals, the development of brain function may be retarded when in infancy the subjects are deprived of suitable challenge, adequate stimulation, the protection of a parent, and opportunities for successful interaction with the environment. There are instances of infants and children raised in relentlessly hostile environments or in environments permitting no continuing human relationship who have not matured. Some, indeed, have acted as idiots. Aged persons deteriorate rapidly when they are deprived of their work and social responsibilities and this may not be entirely attributable to anatomic changes in heart and blood vessels or to a breakdown of the neuron as the organism grows older. Indeed, there is evidence to suggest that the accumulated effects of long years of anxiety, repression, frustration, and the indefinite postponement of satisfaction may be related to the difference between poor performance of many older persons and the better performances of the relatively few who have had, and continue to have, fulfilled and satisfactory life experiences.

In laboratory animals, catastrophes or continued stressful circumstances are followed by the loss of previously stable conditioned reactions. Rats, pressed almost to exhaustion by being forced to swim for fifty hours may, after recovery, exhibit permanent cycles of activity and inactivity suggestive of periodic overactive or depressed phases of human behaviour. Wild rats induced to fight each other to the point of exhaustion may in like manner permanently show cycles of under and over-activity. Such prolonged and stressful swimming and fighting may damage the brain.

In man total isolation and severely restricted sensory stimulation are followed by temporary impairment of high level brain functions. Men subjected to the prolonged abuse and hatred of their fellows, as in prison, behave as though their heretofore actively functioning brains were severely damaged. They pass through predictable states of progressive impairment, comparable to the impairment observed in subjects with progressive loss of brain substance. Complete isolation, lack of opportunity to talk, repeated failure, frustration, and the revilement of other men clouds the mind, may make a man confabulate, become more suggestible, cause him to rationalize behaviour previously unacceptable, or abandon his value system for one utterly incompatible with his former principles.

We have inquired as to how much the brain shares in the damaging effects of prolonged stress. It was found that persons with no evidence of gross anatomic disease of the brain but with longstanding anxiety and other disturbances in behaviour and mood (both with and without bodily disorders) also had severe thinking and adaptive difficulties. Indeed, they performed in work-a-day circumstances and in test procedures as though massive amounts of brain had been damaged or removed. Those with effective defences such as blaming, rationalizing, sublimation, denying, pretending, or withdrawing from participation, showed less deterioration in brain function. But when these defences were no longer adequate or stress had been too prolonged, these individuals, too, acted as though their mental processes had led to alteration in the material substrate of the brain.

Change as Equivalent to Threat

Among the many circumstances perceived as threatening one of the most outstanding is change itself. Rapid and violent social change, by disrupting established relationships, constitutes a serious threat. The development of frustrations and conflicts is minimized in societies where social hierarchies and the individual's place in life are clearly defined, and generally known and accepted. It is not the specific behaviour toward parents, power, possession, sexuality, the hours of work, or even the type of work or the amount of individual freedom of action, that becomes pertinent to the development of stress with its ensuing reaction patterns and disease. It is the unresolved frustrations and conflict engendered by the culture.

An amusing observation relevant to the effects of rapid change was made on Hopi Indians. A young Hopi, American schooled, may be contrasted with his father. His father believed that when he trod on the track of a snake, he would get sore ankles unless he took himself to the medicine man, who could prevent this by incantation. But in contrast, his American-schooled son, who no longer believes in the powers of the medicine man (considering him a humbug) and refuses to consult him, does get sore ankles after walking in the track of a snake. This implication is clear, that in a rapidly changing society, anxiety-inducing factors outlive anxiety-resolving factors.

There is evidence that disruptive changes may be relevant to infectious processes. High mortality from tuberculosis has been associated with increased industrialization during the nineteenth and twentieth centuries and the resulting migrations from rural to urban life and from one country to another. The high mortality has usually been considered the result of exposure to cold and rain, lack of food, excessive effort, crowding, and contact of an immigrant population with new and fresh sources of infections to which they had developed insufficient immunity. However, this explanation may not be a sufficient one. When a sizable block of Ireland's population emigrated to American seacoast cities, they were better fed and had more promise for the future. Yet the death rate from tuberculosis among the Irish in New York City, for instance, was twice as much as at the same time in Dublin.

Perhaps we can learn something from the fact that periods of great duress bring about the decline of some diseases and the increase of others? For example, successful Dutch merchants who had peptic ulcers before incarceration in German concentration camps lost their stomach lesions under the horrendous conditions that augmented other diseases. (Sadly, I add, many regained their peptic ulcers upon returning to 'Main Street'.)

In addition to peptic ulceration, mucous colitis, asthma, and upper airway disorders including the common 'rhinitis' dwindled to negligible significance. In one concentration camp psychoneuroses, such as phobias and compulsive-obsessive neuroses, disappeared under the evil conditions of camp or diminished to inconspicuous proportions. Few new instances developed in the camp. However, several months after their release, some of the former inmates whose long-standing neuroses had disappeared while they were in prison again developed their former symptoms. It seems clear, therefore, that all burdens do not have equal significance, nor do all evoke the same adaptive responses.

Recently, we have been seeking answers to some of these questions. A large-scale study of men and women in the context of their environment, and its relationship to their health, has been made by a group headed by Dr Lawrence Hinkle, working in the Human Ecology Program at the New York Hospital and Cornell University Medical College. In this research the life stories of approximately 3,500 ostensibly healthy people were analyzed. Of these 1,700 were semi-skilled American working women, about 1,500 skilled American working men, 100 were Chinese graduate students and professional people selected because they represented a rapidly moving group required to remain in America for political reasons, 74 were Hungarian refugees similarly violently plucked out of their setting, and there was a fifth group of 132 recently graduated from American colleges who were preparing themselves for a life of being executives. The 3,200 or so skilled and semi-skilled American workers were studied over a period of twenty-five years, and their records of absences and health were used, as well as the study of the individuals themselves at the time that this work was more intensively undertaken. Therefore we have the day-by-day rate of illness and the circumstances in which this occurred.

The Chinese group were studied in terms of their memory of their past, as were the Hungarian refugees and the American college students.

We found that episodes of illness — and by illness we mean any symptomatic disorder, whether it be so-called medical, surgical, psychiatric or, to some extent, social — were not distributed at random among the members of any of these groups. In each group during two decades of young adult life approximately a quarter of the individuals had experienced more than one-half of all the episodes of illness that had occurred among all the people. It is extraordinary that in twenty odd years some individuals exhibited twenty days of sickness disability and equally effective and acceptable workers on the other hand exhibited as much as 1,400 days of disability.

As the number of episodes of illness experienced by the individual increased the number of different types of disease syndromes he exhibited increased also. Likewise, as the number of episodes he experienced increased he exhibited illnesses of an increasing variety of aetiologies. He was likely to have more major, irreversible and life-endangering illnesses as well as more minor, reversible, and transient illnesses. Illnesses, therefore, seemed to be a unit, or at least looking upon them this way made more sense than in the usual way of dividing them up according to aetiology or organ systems. Finally, as the number of bodily illnesses increased the number of emotional disturbances, psychoneurotic and psychosomatic disturbances, also increased.

If one examines the illness patterns of men and women over many years one finds that each person has a rather predictable rate of illness. However, from time to time there occur peak periods usually of several years' duration during which the episode rate may be much higher. If we call such peak periods 'clusters of illness' we define a 'cluster year' as a year during which the illness episode rate was at least 1·75 times greater than the average for that individual. We find that about three-fourths of the people show the phenomenon of clustering. We also find that, of those people who show the phenomenon of clustering, about one-eighth of the years of their life span are 'cluster years', and that about one-third of each person's illnesses occur during these years.

If we look at the clusters, we find that they are usually not made up of a single syndrome. Sometimes they consist of a major illness and other illnesses which are commonly thought of as complications. But the usual cluster is made up of several different and ostensibly unrelated syndromes of different degrees of severity, often arising from several aetiological sources, that have no evident relationship to each other. Cluster periods occur at no special time of adult life and have no specific duration or magnitude.

As you might expect, if a Hungarian were seized by the police in 1949 and imprisoned until 1952, beaten, underfed, overworked and exposed to the elements, he might have had pneumonia several times, severe dental caries and a disease with the clinical characteristics of rheumatic fever. Or an American working man who became alcoholic might develop malnutrition, cirrhosis, oesophageal varices, and have a number of accidents. But actually phenomena such as these account for only a small proportion of the clusters of illness that were observed in any group. It was much more common to observe such peak periods of illness in the absence of any significant change in diet, exposure to infection, trauma, toxic materials or other so-called physical aspects of the environment.

The main point is that the great majority of the clusters of illness occurred in the lives of the members of every group at times when they perceived their life situations to be unsatisfying, threatening or overdemanding and productive of conflict, and they could make no satisfactory adaptation to these situations. The situations were in general those which arose out of disturbed relations with family members and important associates, threats to security and status, restrictions and limitations which made it impossible to satisfy important personal needs and appetites.

One might raise the valid objection, that retrospective memory of illness and circumstances perceived to be threatening would be unreliable, and although we have between 2,000 and 3,000 persons with actual records of illness much of our data was retrospective. So we did another kind of study. We took approximately seventy subjects, and all the information relating to their health and illness was separated. This was given to a medical statistician who received no other information about the subjects. Using a pre-arranged standardized procedure he calculated the annual illness episode rates for each subject. Then all of the remaining data on each subject representing the observations of anthropologists, sociologists, psychiatrists, psychologists and the reports of associates and other observers, biographical statements and those portions of the medical data not describing illness (such as non-medical experience, occupations and activities) were separated and given to another group of three observers who did not know the illness episode rate or other details of the medical history. Each of these three, working independently, were asked to predict for each year of the subject's recent life, his perception of his life situation and his ability to make an adequate adaptation to it, using a five-point scale from 'highly satisfactory' to 'highly unsatisfactory'. Altogether 1,234 years of life of these subjects were scored. The ratings of the three observers coincided with each other to a degree far beyond chance. The mean of the three estimates for each year was plotted against the independently derived illness episode rate of the individual for that year. From this it was ascertained that the illness episode rate of the majority of these people was significantly higher during these years when the observers estimated that these people had perceived their total life situations as unsatisfactory.

What reference have these facts to longevity and to death? Our study is still too young to answer this question. But there are hints from other sources that years of life can be pressed out of man by catastrophe or prolonged duress. Most physicians have seen sudden and unexplainable death come to those who are overwhelmed or filled with despair. The complex unitary character of mind-body is shown in the evidence that 'bone-pointing', 'hexing' and excommunication of transgressors of tribal mores may remarkably shorten life if not immediately kill a man. Suitable studies have still not been made to explain such deaths. However, it has been shown that wild rats capable of swimming ninety or more hours may nevertheless die in a few minutes when they have been terrified before being plunged into water. Careful study of the hearts of these creatures revealed that death resulted from a depressive reaction of the nervous system which gradually slowed and ultimately arrested the heart's beat. But should the rat be lifted from the water shortly before the heart stops, it promptly recovers, and may withstand subsequent immersions as well as an average rat.

When male rat interlopers were introduced into established colonies of males and females, they were vigorously attacked by the resident males. Within hours or days after the attack, most of the interlopers died — but not of wounds. Some of them had been dominant rats in their own colonies. Autopsy revealed that the adrenal glands of the dead interlopers were much enlarged, yet adrenal secretion was depleted. The fact that the interlopers were excluded from the group seemed to make them more vulnerable.

Is there reason to infer that men who experience catastrophes of any kind, but who actually suffer no burns, direct effects of irradiation or physical injury have shorter life spans than others? Do such persons grow twenty years older than their actuarial age?

Though definite answers to these questions await further statistical analysis, we do have precise information from our own records of the World War II and the Korean action concerning the effect on life span and health of prolonged adverse and seriously threatening life experience. Of approximately 7,000 United States prisoners of war captured by the North Koreans, about one third died. Medical observers reported that the cause of death in many instances was ill-defined and was referred to by the prisoners as 'give-up-itis'. Death seemed to be the end result of infection, depletion, exhaustion, serious demoralization, humiliation, despair, and deprivation of human support and affection. The prisoner simply became apathetic, listless, neither ate nor drank, helped himself in no way, stared into space, and finally died.

A recently completed study of the effects of imprisonment on Americans during World War II furnished revealing information about approximately 94,000 United States prisoners of war who were taken in Europe. These men were imprisoned for about ten months. Less than one per cent. of them died before liberation. In contrast, in the Pacific theater, about 25,000 Americans became prisoners of war. They remained in prison four times as long as those captured in Europe, and suffered far more threats, abuse, and humiliation. Their demoralization was often extreme. More than one third of them died in prison.

Six years after liberation, the fate of those that survived the Japanese prison experience was investigated. In the first place the total number of deaths in the group during these six years was more than *twice* the expected incidence for a similar group of persons not so exposed, and *three times* as great as in the group of United States prisoners of war in Europe. Moreover, the causes of death included many diseases not directly related to confinement or starvation. Twice the expected number died of heart disease, more than twice the expected number of cancer, more than four times the expected number of diseases of the gastrointestinal tract. Twice the expected number died from suicide — and most striking of all — three times the expected number died as a result of accidents. Nine times the expected number died of pulmonary tuberculosis.

It was also found that the admission rate to veterans' hospitals of the former prisoners of war of the Japanese was closely related to the amount of stress endured during imprisonment. Those who had experienced less duress had admission rates only slightly higher than the European prisoners of war. But those who had suffered greatly had far the greatest number of admissions, amounting to seven times as many as did those who had not been prisoners — and 'very poor health' interfered with work in one half. Those that were in 'very poor health' had many different diseases, among them many that did not appear to be immediately related to incarceration — hernia, deafness, and diseases of bones, muscles, and heart. There were ten times as many 'impairments' as among the European prisoners of war.

A general inference has been drawn. In the first place, there is no basis for assuming that illness may be divided into psychosomatic and other illness, except in the most superficial sense. As far as our data are concerned there is no basic or qualitative difference between peptic ulcer, typhoid fever, carcinoma of the breast, or gout in the way that these diseases are related to the patient's general adaptation and his reaction to his circumstances as he perceives them. Granted that the individual with peptic ulcer more readily reflects from day to day or week to week the circumstances of his setting and his perception of himself as threatened, this is a quantitative rather than a qualitative difference. Indeed, if one put aside those instances of grave inborn functional or structural error that early in life narrowly limit the range of adaptability, either at the simple biological or at the more complex neurobiological level, then it may be said that the majority of symptomatic illnesses, medical, surgical and psychiatric, arise in or may be remarkably influenced by environmental circumstances perceived by the individual concerned as threatening.

DISCUSSION

Dr Lacey challenged the notion that in reacting to a noxious stimulus the stress-sensitive organisms' bodily responses were appropriate in kind but inappropriate in amount. He described this as 'a value judgment based upon traditional physiology'. If the responses were viewed from some other frame of reference than that of homeostatis they might be found not to be inappropriate in amount but to be serving functions and purposes which we did not at present understand. He pointed out also that bodily stress responses similar to those described by Professor Wolff in the severe traumas of bereavement, incarceration, etc. could also be seen in the less dramatic circumstances of persons faced with the task of rapidly performing mental arithmetic in a social situation where success was expected of them.

Subsequent discussion ranged around the definition of stressor and stress. Professor Hargreaves objected to defining a stress in terms of a noxious stimulus because one could not say whether a stimulus was noxious or not until one knew its outcome in terms of psychological failure or success. Professor Harold Wolff replied that one judged that a stress was present by the *response* of the organism, that is by the type and intensity of the reaction 'but by no means by the stimulus unless one knows the subject very well.'

Professor G. W. Harris asked which reactions then should be taken as characterizing the presence of stress; should one, for example, include the orienting response accompanied by autonomic manifestations in a dog?

Professor Selye agreed with Professor Wolff that a stress reaction must be appraised by its consequences since it depends upon the subject whether he will appreciate something as a stressor or not and since so many agents, from simple mechanical trauma through the whole of pharmacology into psycho-social factors, can produce a reaction. Measurable indices of the stress reaction included enlargement of the adrenal cortex, atrophy of the thymus and disappearance of lymphocytes and eosinophils in the blood. He added that, in his opinion, 'everything that produces an increase in the rate of wear and tear on the body is a stressor; life is impossible in the absence of stress; only death relieves us of all stress; the secretion of our glands, the beat of our hearts, are stressor agents.' Thus, stress may also be defined as, or at least related to, the rate of wear and tear or the utilisation of the body's machinery.

Dr Russell Davis described the way in which humans react to stressful situations as a sequence of four phases. First, there is a mobilization of resources, the activation of emergency mechanisms with a heightening of responsiveness, an increase in the extent and force of responses and a feeling of excitement and effort. These emergency mechanisms tend to bring with them an impairment of skill since they are suited more to the cruder physical dangers of the past than to the intricate situations met with in civilized living which demand subtle, co-ordinated, finely judged responses. As activity rises to a peak of intensity the second phase ensues when repeated stimulation without reinforcement leads to a reduction in responsiveness accompanied by withdrawal and depression. The third stage is characterized by a compulsive preoccupation with the stressful situation during which the subject talks repetitiously about it. Through this phase new defences emerge to constitute the last stage of the reaction. Dr Russell Davis pointed out that in the fourth stage there is not a return to the pre-stress state. If a stress is applied to an organism and then removed the organism, unlike the material in the physical stress-strain system, never returns to the previous state of affairs. A good analogy would be a sea-wall; when the wall is breached a new wall has to be built which may perhaps be based on the ruins of the old but which is likely to be different from it.

Dr Grey Walter made a similar point. In a physical structure one applies a stress force and the deformation of the system is known as strain. In most materials, when the stress is removed the structure returns to approximately its original state, though continued oscillatory stress produces changes in the material over a long period of time, producing, for example, metal fatigue. There is also a breakdown point at which the structure gives way. In a simple structure at this point there is complete irreversibility; for example, the beam breaks and the load falls through it. But in a complex organism like the human being, when the structure yields at one point the load is caught at another and then at another until finally death may ensue. There is a series of mechanisms each taking the strain at different levels.

Dr Grey Walter asked whether we could not design experiments to identify these mechanisms. Pavlov, for example, had attempted to define some of them operationally, describing his animals in terms of 'stability', 'strength' and 'versatility'. Perhaps in the experimental psychological laboratory an approach through cybernetical or general systems theory would result in a unified language in which these parameters could be usefully measured.

Dr Richter added the following definitions of the word 'Stress' in different fields:

SOME CURRENT USAGES OF THE WORD 'STRESS' IN DIFFERENT FIELDS

Derek Richter

Common Language

(1) The word stress, probably derived from 'distress', was used originally for any kind of hardship, burden, pressure or compulsion inflicted on a person or on a material object. A stress produces characteristically a condition of tension

or strain in the person or object affected by it. The word is now used loosely in several different senses for (2) pressure or emphasis (as in the phrase *to lay stress on*) and particularly for (3) an *adverse force*, pressure or influence. The word is also used for (4) the *state* or *condition* of a person subjected to adverse influences causing tension or strain, and (5) a *state of affairs* or general situation characterized by adverse influences.

By 'the stress of modern living" is generally understood the sum total of irksome obligations, duties, and social conventions, together with any other conditions of living that may give rise to worry, tensions, anxiety, conflict or frustration. Mental stress may also arise for specific reasons, as in an individual who holds beliefs that are in conflict with the views of those in authority.

Physics

(6) Stress is a physical pressure applied to a body so as to cause a deformation of the body: the deformation is called strain. Stress is measured by the force applied per unit area, or dynes per sq. cm. in c.g.s. units. The dimensions of stress are $M L^{-1} T^{-2}$. The strain is expressed as the ratio of the change of length to the original length $\frac{dl}{l}$ along any axis: the dimensions of strain are unity. The ratio of stress to strain is a characteristic constant of a body: it is known as the modulus of elasticity.

Biology

(7) Stress may be defined as anything constituting a threat, real or apparent, to the biological integrity of the organism. Stress depends partly on factors in the environment and partly on the vulnerability of the individual. There are environmental factors that constitute a stress for one individual and may not be stressful for another who is less sensitive or better able to adapt.

Physiology

(8) An environmental agent or influence, affecting an organism adversely. The word stress is used here in sense (3) of the common language, for agents such as heat, cold, etc. (The term *stressor agent* or *stressor* is now commonly used by physiologists for a stress in this sense of the word.)

(9) Stress has been defined as the *state* or *condition* of an organism subjected to a load of such strength as to cause a depletion of reserves greater than can be restored in the time available for recovery.

In other words, stress is the state of an organism subjected to pressures to which its homeostatic mechanisms cannot readily enable it to adapt.

(10) The word stress is also used by some physiologists to describe the *disturbance* or *strain* produced in an organism subjected to a load (Gerard, 1957). In this sense of the word, a stress can be described in terms of the displacement of factors such as blood pressure, blood metabolite levels, etc. which are controlled by the homeostatic mechanisms.

(11) The language relating to stress was systematized by Selye (1950) who introduced the terms *stressor agent* or *stressor* for an adverse influence that acts on

an organism thereby producing a *condition* of stress. In such a *stress situation*, the organism reacts by a defense reaction, or *stress response*. Stress is then defined as the state or condition of an organism subjected to a stressor sufficient in strength to cause damage or elicit a defense reaction. Terms such as birth stress, cold stress, etc. refer to the condition of an organism subjected to these influences.

Stressors include heat, cold, haemorrhage, anoxia, irradiation, toxic factors and psychological traumata, which act on the whole organism, and burns, local infections, wounds, etc., which act locally. Stressors are thus factors to which the organism needs to adapt in order to avoid or minimize the damage that may be caused by them.

Psychology

(12) Stress is the state or condition of an organism whose reaction to the environment is characterized by anxiety, tension, or a defensive behavioural response. Under these conditions the individual may build up defense mechanisms to reduce his anxiety or to defend himself against it.

Stress itself is an abstract concept derived partly from subjective experience and partly from the observation of overt stress responses in situations that elicit them. The concept of stress may be coloured by views held about the situations that occasion stress and about the psychological mechanisms involved in reacting to it.

Psychological stress situations are generally characterized by a conflict of incentives or of basic drives to which the individual is compelled to adapt. There may be an apparent threat to self-esteem or to security, as when achievement falls short of expectations. Mental stress may be chronic, as for example in unhappy human relationships and long-standing conflicts over religious, political or racial beliefs: or stress may be acute, as in the stress of a cross-examination or the sudden loss of a lover or of a child.

Stress may be produced in an individual experimentally by methods such as giving an insoluble problem to solve. A comparable stress situation can be obtained in animal conditioning experiments in which an animal is made to attempt a discrimination that is too difficult for it. Prolonged stress of this kind can lead to the development of complex defense reactions described as 'experimental neuroses'. The reaction of psychological stress depends in general on constitutional factors making up the personality and particularly on the capacity to adapt by modifying the established pattern of behavioural response.

Stress may be consciously experienced as such, or it may be unconscious and recognized only by the after-effects. Thus an individual may push himself beyond the limits of his endurance without being consciously aware of the stress and thereby impose on himself a burden from which it may take him some time to recover. The extent to which stress is consciously experienced varies greatly from one individual to another, depending on personality traits as well as on the nature of the stress situation involved.

EFFECTS OF TRAINING UNDER STRESS IN CHILDREN

E. J. ANTHONY

Institute of Psychiatry, University of London[1]

Confronted by an assembly of eminent scientific men, it requires quite a difficult shift in perspective to see them, in the mind's eye, as the drooling, demanding, incontinent infants that they once all were. Within the period of a few decades, a metamorphosis has occurred as striking as any other in the biological order, and it is my purpose here to examine some of the alleged stresses entailed in the transformation of an autistic, egocentric, pleasure-driven infant into a socially-conforming, considerate, and reality-orientated adult.

I shall peg my investigations to a very simple conceptual model; one that has been used in the past by Freud, Piaget, and the stimulus-response theorists among others. It is the model of a reacting organism in its environment, exposed to stimulation, and discharging itself periodically so as to maintain its homeostasis.

There are three essential parts to this model: the afferent component comprising the play of impulses on the organism; the central component reflecting the sensitivity of the organism; and the efferent component concerned with the adequacy of the discharge.

In my first example, I shall describe the state of affairs at the afferent end, where, at normal times, conditions of over-stimulation or under-stimulation may prevail. I am not going to talk here about the under-stimulation stresses. A great deal of work has already been done on them, and such concepts as 'contact hunger' and 'stimulus deprivation' have emerged in relation to certain pathological states of separation, institutionalism, hospitalism and sensory isolation. My concern is with over-stimulation, where it reaches a traumatic level. With regard to this, the following general hypothesis can be formulated: certain stresses occurring at certain stages of development and in a certain dosage will overwhelm certain children and produce certain characteristic disorganizations of behaviour.

Related to this hypothesis was an investigation that I carried out into sleep

[1] *Present address:* Dept. of Child Psychiatry, Washington University, St Louis.

disturbances. These have been for some time regarded as stress disorders having certain traumatic antecedents in the early history of the child and certain consequences that occur subsequently during the night at a later stage.

TABLE 1

CLASSIFICATION OF SLEEP DISTURBANCES

(Clardy and Hill)

Type 1	Minor disturbances (restlessness, mumbling, talking, teeth grinding, early or frequent waking, difficulty in falling asleep) . . .	46%
Type 2	Nightmares	7%
Type 3	Night terrors	2%
Type 4	Sleep walking	1%
Type 5	Nocturnal enuresis	26%

Various combinations may occur. De Sanctis described two varieties of a nocturnal syndrome—epileptic (which includes the epileptic attack, nightmares, and hypnogogic hallucinations) and hysterical, this latter having an 'inner mental determination'.

Let me first remind you of the clinical features of sleep disturbances. In Table 1 they are classified into minor and major disturbances, the major ones being relatively infrequent as compared with the minor ones. The latter are more usually referred to the general practitioner than to the child psychiatrist.

TABLE 2

AGE PATTERNING IN A SAMPLE OF CHILDREN WITH SLEEP DISTURBANCES

Type of Disturbance	Age Groups			Totals
	4-7	8-10	11-14	
Night terrors. . .	18 63%	7 24%	5 13%	30
Nightmares . . .	3 19%	11 69%	2 12%	16
Sleepwalking. . .	1 5%	6 30%	13 65%	20
Totals . . .	22	24	20	66

N = 66

The age incidence is shown in Table 2, and has a special significance for this study. In our sample, night terrors occurred with greatest frequency in the age period of four to seven, nightmares in the age period eight to ten, and sleep walking in the eleven to fourteen group. There is thus a definite developmental patterning. This confirms the findings of other workers.

The experimental sample was made up of sixty-six cases, all taken in sequence from the clinic waiting list. Not every case was included, however, in the study. One intentional bias lay in the exclusion of any mixed cases exhibiting both nightmares and sleep walking. There were altogether five such cases. The remainder were fairly 'pure' examples of the three main groups. The ratio of girls to boys varied with the age group; one to two in age group one, one to four in age group two, and one to twenty in age group three. Thus there was a relatively high incidence of girls in the first age group and a relatively low incidence of girls in the third age group, the latter incidence reflecting their almost complete absence from the sleep walking group. The children were all first seen as out-patients, but from time

DEPTH OF SLEEP IN RELATION TO SLEEP DISTURBANCES

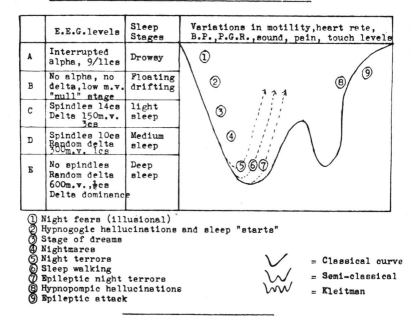

	E.E.G.levels	Sleep Stages	Variations in motility,heart rate, B.P.,P.G.R.,sound, pain, touch levels
A	Interrupted alpha, 9/11cs	Drowsy	
B	No alpha, no delta,low m.v. "null" stage	Floating drifting	
C	Spindles 14cs Delta 150m.v. 3cs	light sleep	
D	Spindles 10cs Random delta 300m.v. 1cs	Medium sleep	
E	No spindles Random delta 600m.v.,½cs Delta dominance	Deep sleep	

① Night fears (illusional)
② Hypnogogic hallucinations and sleep "starts"
③ Stage of dreams
④ Nightmares
⑤ Night terrors
⑥ Sleep walking
⑦ Epileptic night terrors
⑧ Hypnopompic hallucinations
⑨ Epileptic attack

         = Classical curve
         = Semi-classical
         = Kleitman

FIG. 1.—Depth of sleep in relation to sleep disturbances.

to time some were admitted to the in-patient unit of the Maudsley Hospital to check their sleep records and establish depth of sleep curves.

Control cases were also taken off the general waiting list and could be generally described as neurotic children without sleep disturbances. Children from the two groups were matched in terms of age, sex, and intelligence quotients to within ten units. Comparison, therefore, lay between neurotic children who suffered from sleep disturbances and neurotic children who had no such symptoms, the neurosis being the common denominator. They could also be regarded as two different symptom groups, the one suffering from sleep disturbances and the other from disorders of other functions such as elimination, feeding, and motility.

Fig. 1 shows the way in which these disturbances tend to occur during some particular part of the sleep curve. The depth of sleep has usually been assessed in two ways — by the arousability of the subject in response to different perceptual stimuli (sound, touch, etc) and by the epiphenomena associated with sleep (variations in heart rate, respiratory rate, skin resistance, body temperature, and the electrical status of the cortex). There is no doubt that arousability is the more reliable criterion of the depth of sleep. The epiphenomena probably reflect many other psycho-physical events of the sleeping state and may therefore show variable responses. Among the concomitant phenomena, motility is perhaps the best guide. Arousability and motility were the two criteria selected for use in this present study.

The sleep curve varies throughout life. The curve found in childhood differs radically from that found in the adult or from that found in old age. Most parents of young children soon discover that sleep appears to be at its deepest during the early part of the night from between one to two hours after the onset of sleep, and that thereafter the children become more and more arousable. This applies particularly to the younger child. This simple observation was born out by our investigation, which produced a type of curve different from that found by Kleitman (1939) in the adult. In general, it is a smooth curve with one or two humps, the second hump usually appearing later in childhood. There are, of course, variations with the time of the year, the room temperature, the body temperature, the state of the digestive tract, the fullness of the bladder, and so on, but these make less impact on the child's curve than on the adult's curve.

The location of disturbances along this curve was derived from various sources — hospital sleep records, parental sleep records, and information obtained from various authoritative texts. Fig. 1 is a composite picture that attempts to correlate several factors — time of sleep, duration of sleep, sleepfulness and arousability, and the proclivity to disturbances. It will be seen that the anguished cry in the night that summons the parent to the bedroom may arise in several different ways, all previously subsumed under the single heading of 'nightmare'. It may stem from illusional fears during the pre-sleep period in a darkened room, from hypnogogic hallucinations or night starts during the 'floating phase', from nightmares or anxiety dreams during light sleep, and finally, from night terrors at the time of deepest sleep. There is reasonable evidence, judging from electro-encephalographic records during sleep, that dreaming occurs predominantly in the stage of light to moderate sleep. There is also experimental evidence that night terrors can be induced by offering a fearful stimulus to a child after

4

arousing him suddenly into half-wakefulness from deepest sleep. The clinical state produced in this way possesses all the features of the naturally occurring night terror. Manacéine (1897) found that the phenomenon could be brought about if the duration of the induced hypnogogic phase was of sufficient length, and if the child was between the ages of four to seven and showed a tendency to neurotic instability. She related the results to the degree of suggestibility, mentioning that cataleptic phenomena and subsequent amnesia were prominent features of the condition induced.

TABLE 3

POSSIBLE CHAINS OF CIRCUMSTANCES

Unhappy 'Neurotogenic' Home Circumstances

Hypothesis 1	Hypothesis 2	Hypothesis 3	Hypothesis 4	Hypothesis 5
Maternal unreadiness for birth	. Crowded home conditions	. Increased parental aggression	. Restricted living space	. Direct seduction, desertion, separation, etc.
Traumatic birth—physical (Pasamanick) emotional (rank)	. Primal scene— premature exposure to adult sexuality	. Premature exposure to adult violence	. Daytime suppression (noise, mess, movement, etc.)	. Psychological trauma

Increased anxiety, fearfulness and tension— the neurotic character of the stress-sensitive child   . Neurotic disturbances of sleep— night terrors, nightmares, sleepwalking, sleeptalking

The theories of causation of sleep disturbances that have been put forward in the literature are summarized in Table 3. Some of the theorists have considered that a traumatic birth experience (either in a physical or emotional context) might be a predisposing factor; others that precocious exposure to adult sexuality, such as in the 'primal scene' hypothesis, or to experience of adult violence, as, for example, with drunken brawling, might trigger off a response; and others still have referred to daytime suppression of noise, mess and movement; to the occurrence of separation, migration, and hospitalization traumata; and to the effects of global disturbances as divorce, death, disease, and other such disasters. In none of these postulates are predisposing and precipitating factors clearly differentiated.

We looked to see how our experimental group differed from the control neurotic group in these respects to ascertain whether any environmental factors played a specific and possibly causal role in this particular syndrome. Table 4 sums up the differences. Only three alleged factors show a significant difference of incidence. The first of these, the duration in the parental bedroom, is open to misinterpretation in that one was never sure whether the

TABLE 4

POSSIBLE CLINICAL FACTORS IN CAUSATION OF SLEEP DISTURBANCE

Differences between the sleep-disturbed group and neurotic controls

Alleged Cause	Sleep Disturbance Group	Neurotic Control Group	Significance
Duration parental bedroom over two years	35%	16%	0·01
Interparental aggression . . .	43%	39%	NS
Suppression day activities . . .	26%	20%	NS
Trauma (separation etc) . . .	64%	40%	0·05
Phobic mother	73%	34%	0·01
Sibling birth	23%	25%	NS
Family history of mental illness .	19%	22%	NS
Undue parental pressures . . .	39%	33%	NS

N = 104

child was moved into the parental bedroom after or before his sleep disturbance. Parents have limited clinical memories and what they do retain is sensitive to the implications contained in the questions put to them. The phobic mother makes for a genuine difference, and one finds in comparing a check list of fears admitted to by mother and child that a high degree of correspondence exists between them, leading to more than a suspicion that there is a constant communication of fear in progress within the relationship.

The incidence of traumata, chiefly of separation and hospitalization, also shows some difference between the sleep disturbance children and the neurotic controls.

The sleep-disturbed child must be considered a classical type of stress-sensitive child. The term 'sensitive' occurs in the clinical description more

TABLE 5

TRAIT HYPOTHESES

Differences in reactivity between the sleep-disturbed group (S.D.G.)
and the neurotic control group (N.C.G.)

Trait Hypothesis	Test	Sig.
S.D.G. more excitable. .	Profile recognition . . .	NS
S.D.G. more tense . .	Profile recognition . . . Check list tension habits Carbon pressure	0·05
S.D.G. more 'emotional' .	Profile recognition . . .	NS
S.D.G. more fearful . .	Profile recognition . . . Check list by mother and child Fear stimulus	0·01
S.D.G. more egocentric .	3 mountain test (Piaget) . .	NS
S.D.G. more suggestible .	Ink blot suggestion . . .	0·01
S.D.G. more imaginative .	Griffith's method . . . Open-end story	0·10

N = 86

frequently than with any other clinical syndrome. Along with this epithet, there is a conglomeration of other emotional traits which have been described, and we looked to see how far these traits were peculiar to this syndrome.

Table 5 shows an investigation into the trait hypothesis, picking out for comparison traits of excitability, tenseness, emotionality, fearfulness, ego-centricity, suggestibility and imaginativeness. Here again we found that fearfulness was the major point of difference between the experimental and control groups. The sleep-disturbed children were also more suggestible and more tense.

So far it seemed that we were dealing with the fearful child of a fearful mother, but we still had no idea why any particular fearful child was disposed to nightmares, night terrors, or sleep walking. In the pilot investigation conducted on these children, one positive clinical feature that emerged with striking frequency was that the night terror and nightmare groups tended, as a whole, to dream more frequently and more vividly than the sleep walkers, and when we gave them a projective card showing a sleeping child, and asked them to make us some artificial dreams, it became apparent that the night terror and nightmare groups tended to produce more realistic, more vivid, more frequent, and more unpleasant dream material than the children who walked in their sleep. On the basis of these clinical findings, we were led to postulate that the symptom choice was related in some way to the imaginal capacity, and that there was an interdependence between the night and day imagery.

With such postulates in mind, it seemed logical to investigate some of the basic imaginal processes of childhood, and as a guide to selection, we took as a conceptual model the schema as shown in Fig. 2, featuring the possible enhancements of the image as it circulates hypothetically through the visual and cortical pathways.

The children were then tested for these various imaginal capacities. The first was for eidetic imagery, making use of the classical Jaensch techniques. Following on this, came a battery modified from Loewenfeld and Piaget, exploring the visual versus the haptic or stereognostic tendency. On testing, visual subjects are shown to be better observers; they perceive more objectively; they are more impressionistic in their observations; they are more at home with visual stimuli and tend to be bewildered in the dark; they are predominantly extroversive, their primary concern being with the external world; they are better able than haptics to synthesize a partial or moving visual experience and more skilful in representing objects correctly and in proper perspective in space; in contrast, they tend to transform all their haptic experiences into visual ones. Clinically, they are more liable to suffer from visual types of hallucination.

PARADIGM OF THE CIRCUIT OF IMAGERY

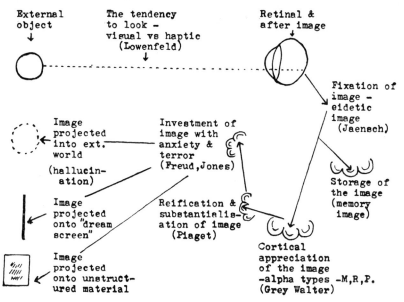

FIG. 2.—Paradigm of the Circuit of Imagery.

In addition to testing for eidetic imagery and visual typing, we made use of Piaget's method of clinical interrogation to assess the degree of dream realism that the children showed.

TABLE 6

VISUAL TENDENCIES

Test Reaction	NT	NC	Sig	NM	NC	Sig	SW	NC	Sig
Strongly eidetic . .	. 88%	64%	0·05	. 81%	44%	0·05	. 35%	40%	NS
Strongly visual . .	. 68%	32%	0·01	. 75%	56%	0·10	. 25%	50%	NS
Marked realism . .	. 72%	68%	NS	. 25%	19%	NS	. 10%	5%	—
Intense dream imagery .	. 68%	56%	NS	. 71%	53%	NS	. 15%	55%	0·01

N = 132   Mean age: 7·6   Mean age: 8·9   Mean age: 10·7

NT = Night terror cases   SW = Sleep walking cases
NM = Nightmare cases   NC = Neurotic controls

The results are summarized in Table 6. Night terror and nightmare groups show themselves to be more strongly eidetic and more strongly visual than the neurotic controls. The sleep walkers, on the other hand, are less eidetic and visual than the neurotic controls.

Our findings would, therefore, support the view that in our experimental sample we were dealing with a group of stress-sensitive children who had reacted to certain traumata in their past lives by developing sleep disturbances. Depending on whether the imaginal processes were highly developed or not, the disturbances could take either a visual form (night terrors and nightmares) or motor form (sleep walking). (Anthony, 1959.)

So far we have been dealing with afferent stimulation and organismic sensitivity. I now want to discuss certain problems pertaining to the discharging end of the model and, on this occasion, I am less concerned with over-discharge as illustrated by the brain damaged child who produces catastrophic amounts of discharge than with the inhibition of discharge. Here again I am not concerned with physical inhibitions, such as swaddling, cradling, plaster immobilizations, or mechanical restraints against masturbation or thumb sucking, but rather with the child enclosed in a psychological strait jacket through the over-protecting, over-training, and over-controlling behaviour of his over-anxious mother in the field of toilet training. The case for comparison are not normal children. They are subjects who have suffered from under-training and a minimum of control.

TABLE 7

THE PRESSURE OF TRAINING
(based on Huschka's criteria)

HIGH PRESSURE OR COERCIVE
Onset under 8 months
Completed under 18 months
Enforced by physical coercion
(rigid, frequent and protracted potting, beatings, use of suppositories, purgatives, enemata)
Enforced by psychological coercion
(threats, withdrawal of love, inculcation of shame, aversion, fear and guilt)

NORMAL PRESSURE
Onset between 8 months and 23 months
Completion between 18 months and 30 months
Use of co-operative techniques

LOW PRESSURE OR PATHOLOGICAL DEFERMENT
Onset after 24 months
Inconsistent or neglectful techniques

Not only is there a comparison of under-trained and over-trained children, but also of under-training and over-training mothers. In Table 7 three possible types of toilet training given by mothers are listed. There is the high-pressure or coercive type of training, the normal-pressure or co-operative type of training and, finally, a low-pressure or pathologically deferred type of training based on inconsistent and neglectful techniques. Training pressures were assessed partly in terms of age of onset and completion, and partly in terms of physical and psychological coercion.

The response of high-pressure and low-pressure mothers to failure in the potting situation, as signified by encopresis, differed considerably. The attitude of the high-pressure mother and her practical response was unaffected or stimulated by failure, whereas the low-pressure, neglectful mother tended to increase her attitude of laissez-faire — she allowed the child even further latitude in toilet matters.

The high-pressure mother tended to blame the child for its soiling, but the low-pressure mother blamed either herself or her environment, more frequently the latter. The reason for these differences is not difficult to understand. The soiling that results from high-pressure treatment occurs after habit-training has been successfully achieved, so that a period of bowel continence is interposed between the training and the symptom. The mother blames the child, and the child feels guilty and ashamed.

Low-pressure training, on the other hand, generally produces a child who has been soiling continuously from birth onwards without any period of bowel continence. This type of child is singularly free from anxiety, shame, and guilt. The relationships between successful training and bowel dysfunction are summed up in Table 8.

TABLE 8

TYPE OF ENCOPRESIS IN RELATION TO TOILET TRAINING

Type of Encopresis	Coercive Training	Co-operative Training	Neglectful Training
Continuous (N = 30)	26·7%	6·6%	66·7%
Retentive (N = 16)	75%	25%	0%
Discontinuous (N = 30)	63·3%	13·3%	23·4%

Total N = 70

We were next interested to learn what psychological effects stressful training had on the feelings, the fantasies, and the attitudes of the child. Again we made use of Piaget's clinical technique to investigate some of the child's fantasies that were related to his faeces. In the first place, we learned that the younger children had animistic notions connected with bowel function and bowel contents. These animistic ideas were expressed in positive, negative, or neutral terms and were classified as such. We discovered a significant correlation between a coercive type of training and a fearful type of fecal fantasy. In contrast, there was a less marked tendency for the neglectfully trained child to be well disposed towards his faeces.

Our next concern was with the attitude of disgust engendered in the child by the type of training he had experienced, and we proceeded to examine this experimentally by exposing the child to a variety of sensory experiences, all linked to fecal materials and situations. The responses of the children were graded in terms of his capacity to develop an aversion reaction to the smell, sight, sound and touch of fecal objects. These were all designed to simulate excreta in all perceptual characteristics as closely as possible.

TABLE 9

REACTION OF NORMAL CHILDREN TO UNPLEASANT ODOURS

Sample	Ages	No Disgust Reaction	Mixed Reaction	Strong Disgust Reaction
Group I (N = 92) . .	Under 5 .	96·7% .	1·1% .	2·2%
Group II (N = 39) . .	5–6 .	28·2% .	23·1% .	48·7%
Group III (N = 164) . .	6–16 .	7·9% .	14·6% .	77·5%

Total N = 295.   Age range = 1 month to 16 years.
Rural and urban populations.   Boys and girls visiting general hospital.

The reaction of the normal children to unpleasant odours is shown in Table 9. As you will notice, there is a transitional period at five and six during which the normal child swings over into what one might call the culturally acceptable type of disgust reaction.

TABLE 10

REACTION OF ENCOPRETIC CHILDREN TO UNPLEASANT ODOURS

Sample	Ages	No Disgust Reaction	Mixed Reaction	Strong Disgust Reaction	Comment
Continuous group (N = 30) .	4–16 .	83·3% .	10·0% .	6·7% .	Similar to normal pre-school response.
Retentive group (N = 16) .	4–6 .	25·0% .	12·5% .	62·5% .	Exaggeration of normal transitional response.
Discontinuous group (N = 30) .	5–16 .	3·3% .	6·7% .	90·0% .	Exaggeration of normal school child's response.

Total N = 76.   Age range = 4–16.   Boys and girls visiting C.G.C.

In Table 10, the comparative reaction of the encopretic children to unpleasant odours is shown, and it will be observed that in the continuous group there is a strong tendency for the 'attraction' reaction to be high and for the discontinuous group to have strong disgust reactions more frequently than the normal children.

In a word association test, in which the exposure was to neutral words and to words with fecal connotations, the continuous group had more stable reactions and shorter reaction times. They adapted as a whole more rapidly to the stressful situation than did the discontinuous group. This was also true of the psycho-galvanic skin responses.

Colour preferences and colour repulsions were not sufficient to differentiate between the groups, but there was a tendency in the right direction in a comparometer study in which two circles of light required to be matched, a fixed circle containing a picture of a toilet situation (Anthony, 1957).

TABLE II

STRONG AVERSION REACTION FOR DIFFERENT SENSORY MODALITIES

Perceptual Battery	'Continuous' Type (%)	'Discontinuous' Type (%)	Significance of Difference P, in %
Smell . . .	7	90	0·3
Colour . . .	17	14	Not sig.
Touch . . .	21	53	1
Sight[1] . . .	43	67	10
Sound[1] . . .	37	60	10

[1] Long reaction time in the word association sub-test and under estimation in the comparometer test have been interpreted as aversion tendencies.

In Table 11, the results obtained from this battery of tests are summarized. Smell and touch are found to differentiate the groups fairly well, whereas sight and sound – the distance receptors – do so poorly or not at all. It is clear that the most stressfully trained child, the discontinuous child, is also more strongly repulsed by anything connected to that training experience.

TABLE 12

SOCIAL CLASS, CLINICAL TYPE AND AVERSION REACTION

Social Class[1]	I	II	III	IV	V		Totals
'Continuous' . . .	—	—	6	13	11	.	30
'Discontinuous' . . .	2	5	12	7	4	.	30
Strong aversion reaction .	2	3	7	8	2	.	22
Intermediate aversion reaction	—	2	5	6	4	.	17
Weak aversion reaction .	—	—	6	6	9	.	21

$$N = 60$$

[1] According to the Registrar General's system of classification.

The 'continuous' cases are concentrated in the two bottom social groups, whereas the 'discontinuous' cases reach a peak in the third group. The weaker aversion reactions appear to be found in the lower social groups.

In Table 12, the reactions are classified in relation to the registrar-general's social class groups. There is a tendency for the discontinuous type of disturbance and the stronger disgust reaction to be confined to subjects in the middle and upper social groups, and for the continuous disturbances and the weaker reactions to occur more frequently among the lower social classes. Most of the continuous types of cases came from problem families living, one might say, in a mess so that the child was hardly able to distinguish his own soiling from the general dirt of his environment.

DISCUSSION

Dr Grey Walter asked to what extent similar symptoms were found in the siblings of encopretic chidren. Dr Anthony replied that, in the continuously soiling child coming from a problem family, the siblings often had exactly the same symptom. With the discontinuous type, however, things were different. These usually come from better, often middle-class homes where the mother tended to be perfectionistic and seldom had more than two children. One child, usually the older, was the scapegoat child who never did right and was thus quite unlike the sibling. In group discussion with the mothers it emerged that the factors which made the child the scapegoat lay in the relationship between the parents. The mother tended to identify the child with the hated father with such remarks as 'he is just like his father', 'his father is a dirty swine and this boy is exactly the same'.

In reply to a question by Dr Denis Hill as to whether the sleep-disturbed children later experienced more neurotic illness than others, Dr Anthony said that insufficient time had yet passed for a follow-up to be effective. He thought, however, that these children were stress-sensitive and would probably remain so throughout life. There were both environmental and genetic factors concerned in the cause of this sensitivity. Sherman and Jost (1945) had shown that there was a substantial correlation between measurements of autonomic function in identical twins and a somewhat lower correlation in siblings. They had also shown that neurotic children reacted more briskly autonomically to frustration and took a longer time to return to the baseline. His own studies on the psychogalvanic response (Anthony, 1957) showed a similar thing. His studies also supported those of Jones (1935) who found that the younger the child the more likely was there to be a discrepancy between the visceral autonomic and expressive emotional reactions. The more response took place outside the less it occurred inside; and the less the response that took place during the day the more seemed to take place during the night.

CHAPTER 3

DISORGANIZATION OF BEHAVIOUR IN ANIMALS

AN ETHOLOGICAL APPROACH

R. A. HINDE

Department of Zoology, University of Cambridge

Though ethologists have rarely used the terms 'stress' or 'stressor' these terms are relevant to many aspects of behaviour which they have studied. In discussing the ethological approach to stress I shall consider for the most part problems which have arisen from the study of animals in natural or near natural conditions, and in which the stress is due either to simultaneous tendencies to behave in incompatible fashions, or to some form of deprivation.

First let us consider the question of behaviour when the animal has conflicting tendencies to behave in incompatible ways. In laboratory experiments on behaviour the animal is normally controlled as to motivation. Often it is subjected to a deprivation schedule which ensures that one type of motivation is paramount. In nature, on the other hand, the higher animals are rarely single-minded. Even while feeding, a passerine bird is constantly on the look-out for predators, and the extent to which it may venture into the open in search of food may be governed by its fear of them. Such conflicts between incompatible tendencies become most acute in certain social situations, for instance in fighting, courtship and so on.

Consider a territorial song bird: while it is on its own territory it attacks any conspecific male which it sees, and when it is off its territory it flees. On the boundary of the territory these two tendencies, to attack and to flee, are more or less in balance, and it is on the boundary that intense skirmishes develop, each individual alternating between attack and escape behaviour, or showing ambivalent behaviour. (See Hinde and Tinbergen, 1958.)

In these situations the ethologist studies primarily the immediate responses to the stressful situation. The interest of the behaviour pathologist, however, lies in responses which become more or less fixed and more or less divorced from the stressful situation. In nature pathological responses of this type are not common in lower vertebrates, chiefly because the animal either escapes from the stressful situation or dies. However, such fixated responses do sometimes occur in nature and they are frequent amongst animals in experimental situations and in zoos. Two processes seem to be important in their acquisition. The first is avoidance conditioning (e.g. Russell Davis, 1957). Responses acquired by avoidance conditioning have a great resistance to extinction — as though the animal never discovers that if he does not make the response he does not get punished.

The second factor which is important in the fixation of these responses lies in the reinforcing value of the performance of the early stages of a behaviour sequence when its completion is impossible. This has been demonstrated experimentally, for instance in the sexual and feeding behaviour of mammals, where intromission without ejaculation, or ingestion without swallowing, have been shown to have a reinforcing effect (e.g. Sheffield, Wulff and Backer, 1951) — though such learning is sometimes subject to early extinction (Grindley, 1929).

With these two processes in mind we may consider the types of behaviour shown when animals are subjected to conflicting tendencies. I shall draw my examples mainly from amongst birds, but the principles have a wide range of applicability.

The first case to consider is that of the *inhibition of all but one response* or one group of responses.

When a feeding passerine sees a flying predator, feeding is inhibited immediately and the bird flees to cover. This may become established by avoidance conditioning. Thus in Masserman's (1943) experiments on experimental neurosis, some of the cats would not feed in the situation in which they had been frightened, even though they were on the point of starvation. In some cases the inhibition of eating was generalized to situations other than that in which the animal had been frightened.

A second possibility is that the animal may show *intention movements appropriate to only one of the conflicting tendencies*. Intention movements of locomotion are, of course, especially common. In a passerine bird the take-off for flight can be analysed into three phases. In the first it crouches and raises its tail; it then springs upwards, flicks it tail downwards and raises its wings, and in the third phase it beats its wings downwards and raises itself into the air. When these intention movements occur in conflict situations, that is in situations where the animal has tendencies to behave in incompatible ways, they may come to look quite different from the intention movements which normally precede flight. For instance, an incomplete take-off may consist of just the first phase, or the first phase followed by the second phase, or the first and second phases alternating, or the first phase alone held for a long period. Furthermore, the various components of the take-off may become divorced from each other. This is particularly the case with wing and tail movements, which may become dissociated from the other components. Thus the crouch may be associated with several wing flicks instead of with one; or the bird may simply beat its tail without showing any of the other components of the take-off. In such ways the movements shown in these conflict situations may appear to differ from intention movements of flight, though in fact they are derived from them (Andrew, 1956a).

Such intention movements may become fixed as a result of learning. Thus some buntings were kept in cages in which the perches were too near the roof, so that the birds had no room to stretch their necks. Instead of showing the normal intention movements of flight, they developed a peculiar one in which they bent their heads backwards, while remaining somewhat crouched, thus avoiding hitting the roof. This became quite stereotyped and continued when the birds were put in large cages.

Similar things, of course, are very common in zoos. Thus elephants in close confinement often show an unhappy rocking which is derived from an intention movement of locomotion.

The next category of behaviour is that of *compromise behaviour* (Andrew, 1956b). Two types of behaviour which are themselves incompatible may, nevertheless, share some components. Thus, in an approach/avoidance conflict, certain elements of intention movements may be common to both approaching and avoiding: a passerine bird which wants to approach a food dish but is at the same time afraid to do so will beat its tail vigorously, this component being common both to approaching and flying away.

Sometimes the animal shows *alternation between the two incompatible types of behaviour*. Thus in fighting across a territory boundary, each bird attacks and flees in turn. Sometimes the alternation is much more rapid than this; in the pre-copulatory display of the chaffinch, the male has tendencies to mate with the female and to flee from her, and he approaches with a very peculiar zig-zag mincing walk in which he edges a little way towards her, and away again, in rapid succession. I do not know of any cases of this sort of alternation being established by learning in animals, but I dare say there are comparable cases of habitual ditherers in man.

The next category of behaviour is that of *ambivalent posturing*. Many threat or courtship postures which are given in situations which involve incompatible tendencies can be analysed into components, some of which are associated with one of the conflicting tendencies, some with the other, and some with both. An instance is the upright threat posture of the herring gull where the neck is stretched upwards and forwards, the beak down and the wings are raised. These are all intention movements of striking a rival. But as the bird approaches its opponent the neck is slowly withdrawn; this is especially marked in birds which subsequently retire from the skirmish and is in fact an intention movement of retreat. Thus the posture as a whole combines intention movements of both attack and retreat (Tinbergen, 1953).

Such postures are used in social communication and have therefore become modified by natural selection in evolution for efficiency as signals. This has involved changes, collectively known as 'ritualization', in both the form and timing of the movement, and also the evolution of conspicuous structures which are shown off. Although the movement may thus have become much changed in the course of evolution from its original form, comparative study usually enables its evolutionary origin to be traced. Of course I am speaking here of postures which have become fixed in evolution. I cannot give you cases of ambivalent postures which have been fixed in a similar way by learning in individual animals.

The next category is that of *redirection activities*. When an object arouses tendencies for incompatible types of behaviour the animal may redirect one of them on to another object. The female black-headed gull elicits both sexual and aggressive behaviour from her mate, and he may redirect his aggressive behaviour on to a passer-by (Moynihan, 1955). Such re-directed aggression is common in flocks. Hens in a farmyard are normally arranged in a dominance hierarchy such that the alpha bird in the flock can attack and peck all others, the beta bird can attack all except the alpha bird, and so on; when a bird is attacked by its superior it may vent the aggression which its superior arouses on to one of its subordinates. Such behaviour may become fixed, so that the beta bird is often a great tyrant, whereas the alpha bird is merely a benevolent despot.

The final category in this section is that of *displacement activities*. Sometimes an animal, while showing behaviour belonging to one functional group of activities, may suddenly shift to behaviour more usually characteristic of a quite different context. Thus fighting starlings may suddenly start to preen their feathers in the middle of the fight, and various other passerines may show foraging movements during boundary fights or before copulation. These apparently irrelevant types of behaviour are classed as displacement activities. The motor patterns of displacement activities in birds are usually, but by on means always, species characteristic ones, but in other animals individually acquired patterns frequently appear as displacement behaviour.

Displacement activities occur mainly in two types of situation; when the animal is subject to conflicting tendencies, and in situations in which the appropriate external stimulus fails to appear or suddenly disappears. This formerly led to the view that the displacement activity was due to an excess of drive; when the animal was thwarted it was supposed that the excess drive had to find outlet through another channel, and thus the displacement activity appeared (Tinbergen, 1952). The key words used in this type of explanation were 'sparking over': something was said to spark over from one channel to another.

It is now clear that the category of displacement behaviour, which has been extremely useful at a descriptive level, is causally a heterogeneous one In the first place many responses which were formerly classed as displacement activities can now be better placed in other categories. For instance, when great tits are fighting on a territorial boundary they will very often suddenly break off the fight and peck vigorously at the bark or at a bud. I formerly classed this as displacement feeding behaviour, because they feed on the bark or buds, but now think that the behaviour has more in common with a redirection activity; the patterns of pecking at a bud and pecking at a skull happen to be similar, and the animal is venting its aggression on the bud.

In other cases of displacement behaviour the present trend is to look for causal factors common to the situation in which the displacement behaviour occurs and to that in which the same activity occurs in its normal functional context. In fact, the causal factors which evoke displacement behaviour are often much less different from those which evoke the same behaviour in normal contexts than appears at first sight.

Thus Tinbergen (1952) has emphasized that the nature of the activity which appears as a displacement activity in a particular context depends on the stimuli which are present at the time. A fighting turkey may show displacement drinking behaviour if water is present, but displacement feeding behaviour if it is not (Raber, 1948). Both exteroceptive and proprioceptive stimuli may be important in this way.

Recently more detailed analyses along these lines have been made. Andrew (1956b), and Morris (1956) independently suggested that much so-called displacement behaviour is really a consequence of widespread autonomic activity. For instance in spring buntings make sexual chases as part of their courtship behaviour. In these chases the male flies rapidly after the female, but it is evident both before and after the chase that he is very much afraid of her. Before and after the chase the male shows behaviour patterns which normally function in reducing the body temperature. The male and the female have both taken the same amount of exercise, but only the male shows this cooling behaviour, and not the female. It seems, therefore, that the cooling behaviour is related to the fear rather than to the exercise. Sweating in fear in man is presumably a similar thing.

Sometimes this widespread autonomic activity may produce stimuli which evoke further somatic activities. These may appear to be functionally irrelevant although the stimuli present are similar to those which evoke them in their normal context. For instance, the autonomic activity may produce skin stimuli which evoke scratching or preening. No physiological studies have yet been made of such cases, but they are urgently needed.

A second approach to the problem of displacement behaviour has been made by van Iersel and Bol (1958) in their study of displacement preening in terns. When terns are incubating their eggs they sometimes show displacement preening when subjected to mild fear. Van Iersel suggests that the preening is a response to the stimuli which normally evoke preening. Preening is normally elicited by certain external factors which are constantly present in some degree. A strong tendency to incubate inhibits preening, and fear inhibits incubation. When incubation is partially inhibited by fear, its inhibitory effect on preening is reduced, and preening can occur. This seems to be a good behavioural explanation, though some might not agree with the neuro-physiological implications which Dr van Iersel put upon it.

A similar idea of an order of priority of types of behaviour underlies the ethological approach to the homosexual, or rather pseudofemale, behaviour which is shown by some fish and birds when male behaviour is impossible. If ten-spined sticklebacks are crowded in a tank, one male becomes dominant and establishes a territory while the remaining males behave as females (Morris, 1952). This was formerly regarded as a sort of displacement activity and discussed in terms of sparking over, but it is clearly more profitable to look for causal factors common to male behaviour and female behaviour.

Thus the current trend is to analyse the causal basis of each particular example of displacement behaviour, rather than to make generalizations about the causation of them all. Most of the work has so far been concerned with the problem of which apparently irrelevant behaviour pattern appears in a given context, and not with the factors which influence its intensity. In so far as intensity has been discussed, emphasis has been laid on the incompleteness of the displacement behaviour as compared with the strength of the conflicting tendencies which are being thwarted. However, if the causal factors for the displacement behaviour are similar to those which evoke that type of behaviour in its normal context, it is the vigour of some displacement behaviour which is surprising.

In the preceding paragraphs I have neglected many types of behaviour which occur in situations of conflicting tendencies — for instance regression — through lack of time and because they are so much more complicated. However, it seems likely that these also can be tackled in terms of avoidance conditioning, common causal factors, an order of priorities for different types of behaviour and the other principles mentioned above.

In addition, it must be remembered that conflicts of this sort may lead not only to long-term behavioural disorders, but also to long-term physiological effects of a rather different type. For instance, Clarke (1953) subjected voles to stress by placing them in cages with a previously established and aggressive pair for a few hours a day for about a month. Many of them died, but not of wounds — and he found that the adrenal and spleen weights had increased and the weight of the thymus decreased.

Similar studies with captive and wild rats have been made by Christian (1950), Barnett (1958) and others. I will not discuss these effects here, as similar work on man and laboratory animals will perhaps be discussed by Professor Selye and Dr Hoagland later, but I mention them because it is important that psychologists considering the effects of stressful situations should not overlook the physiological picture.

Finally, we may consider briefly the effects of deprivation. Each functional category of behaviour — feeding, fighting, or whatever it is — depends on a series of chains of appetitive behaviour. Each link of appetitive behaviour brings the animal into a situation where the stimuli which evoke the next link in the chain are present. Thus when we speak of deprivation we mean that the stimuli for the next link in the chain are missing. The appetitive behaviour may then become very intense and persistent; and if the appropriate stimuli continue to be absent, various abnormalities may appear.

In the first place, the animal may respond to a normally inadequate object. This may be adaptive from the point of view of natural selection. For instance, it is adaptive for a bird to nest in a sub-optimal site if a perfect site is not available. On the other hand, it is non-adaptive for a male to attempt to mate with a bird of another species if it cannot find a mate of its own.

If such behaviour directed towards a normally inadequate object does appear, learning may occur such that the appetitive behaviour is *always* directed to such inadequate objects. Thus if canaries are deprived of nest material they develop a series of bizarre habits of various types (Hinde, 1956). One of these consists of picking up one of their own feathers and then flying to the nest pan with it and going through the movements of building there, although they never detach a feather from their breast.

Alternatively, they may actually pull the feather out and fly to the nest pan with it and go through the movements of building: next time they go to the nest pan they pick up that feather again, fly backwards and forwards with it a few times and then go back and build with it. In such cases the behaviour may become extremely stereotyped, so that the deprived canary may always fly to exactly the same corner of the cage in order to pick up its own breast feather. One female which was smart enough to attempt to pull out not her own feathers but those of her mate, nearly always concentrated her attention on the third primary on the right wing. She tugged at it for about a fortnight but never got it out.

In these situations learning occurs even though the behaviour never leads to its functional end and no nest is built. The abnormal behaviour may persist even after the deprivation is over. Two chaffinches which were kept without material plucked their own breasts almost completely bare. In two successive summers when they were placed in an outside aviary and had superabundant nest material they disregarded the material and plucked themselves bare again. This is another example of the performance of the early stages of the appetitive behaviour proving reinforcing when the chain cannot be completed. Why these peculiar habits such as picking up your own feathers, or carrying material away from the nest as well as to it, do not occur under normal circumstances is, of course, another problem.

Appetitive behaviour which becomes fixed in this way may become extremely stereotyped and apparently meaningless. Some of these chaffinches which were deprived of material used to hop over the floor of the cage looking for material and going through the movements of picking it up from the floor, and eventually they acquired a tick derived from an intention movement of picking up material which lasted into subsequent seasons.

A similar thing occurs in the stereotypes formed by animals in zoos which are confined behind a line of wire netting. When they are first put into the cage they pace up and down in front of the wire netting and then turn around in a figure of eight. After they have been confined in the cage for a period they make a figure of eight, often some distance from the wire netting and apparently divorced from the desire to get out of the cage, in a way quite different from the initial pacing up and down (Holzapfel, 1939).

One can trace back to their origins in this way many of the compulsive rituals which one sees in animals, but I would not like to give the impression that this can be done in anything like all the cases. Many individuals have compulsive rituals whose origin is quite obscure. One canary at Cambridge always has to write large noughts with her beak on the wall of the cage every time she carries nest material, and a great tit always has to keep pulling a twig back and letting it ping against the side of the wire netting. They are typical compulsive rituals, but their origin is quite obscure.

One other type of abnormal behaviour which occurs in deprived animals should be mentioned — the hypertrophy of those normal patterns which the animal is able to show. For instance, Dr Holzapfel quotes a pine marten which was confined in a rather small cage. This species lays scent marks from its anal glands as part of its normal behaviour. This captive individual visited its scent marks several times a minute in a compulsive fashion instead of once every few hours as a normal one would do. This condition was ameliorated by introducing new valencies into the animal's life by enlarging the cage and so on.

In this paper I have presented only a series of scattered thoughts. Ethologists have concentrated on the description and classification of behaviour in stressful situations, and on comparing the behaviour shown in those situations with the behaviour shown in more normal ones. This, of course, means that the analysis is only at a very elementary stage, but ethologists believe that this description and classificatory analysis is an essential first step before causal hypotheses can be erected.

DISCUSSION

Considerable discussion centred round the relevance for behaviour studies of stimulation or ablation of discrete parts of the brain. Dr Hinde said that work of this sort in relation to ethological work was just beginning in several centres. Lesions were being made and stimulation carried out in the brains of geese and pigeons but one of the difficulties was that ethologists in the past had done so much work with very small animals. Professor G.W. Harris quoted some studies in which the dominant male in a group of monkeys was moved down in the social hierarchy by stimulation through implanted electrodes located in the frontal lobe. When the stimulation was stopped the animal re-acquired his dominance.

Care had to be exercised in interpreting the results of stimulation experiments however. Dr Grey Walter quoted an experiment with chickens in which two electrodes were implanted each in a position appropriate to produce a particular behaviour pattern—one the pecking and feeding and the other the escape by flight produced normally by the appearance of a predator. The hope was that, by stimulating the two electrodes simultaneously, the investigators would produce displacement activity, but this in fact did not occur. This would seem to imply that at least in this case the generation of the displacement activity occurred at a point in the nervous system afferent to that at which the electrodes were inserted. There was general agreement that in some instances stimulation produced behaviour by direct action on a centre integrating that behaviour. Professor Gerard quoted as an example the application of a highly localized stimulation in the infra-orbital region in man leading to completely iterative behaviour. A person counting 'one, two, three, four' if this region was stimulated kept on saying 'four, four, four, four' and, when the stimulation ceased, went on 'five, six, seven, eight, nine'. On the other hand, Professor Selye commented that if a lesion made in a particular part of the brain is followed by a behavioural change, that does not necessarily imply that the area destroyed has anything directly to do with the behaviour observed. For example, if the posterior pituitary lobe is removed the animal drinks a great deal. But nobody thinks that the posterior lobe is a centre for drinking behaviour. Additionally, Dr Grey Walter added, stimulation is a word that is rather glibly used. When one passes currents through electrodes in an animal's brain one may be producing not 'stimulation' but inhibition or an inhibition of an inhibition and so on.

Dr Hinde said that one must also bear in mind the concept of general drive as developed by Hull and others. Ethologists had in the past denied the existence of causal factors common to all activities, and supposed each type of behaviour was influenced only by causal factors specific to it. In practice it seems that stimuli have two types of effect, one general and the other specific to a particular activity or group of activities. It was partly for this reason that Dr Hinde did not agree with Lorenz's 'reservoir' theory in which a certain energy builds up leading, at a certain level, to the release of a specific act of behaviour. Another reason why he disliked this theory was because the centres for behaviour were concerned with integration. Their role in motivation is not proven.

Professor Hargreaves pointed out that change in behaviour could be caused equally by psycho-social as by neurophysiological factors. For example, the pecking order of hens could be changed by a hormone implantation. On the other hand, a female jackdaw, on pairing with a precedent mate, moves up to the pecking place of her mate even though she was at the bottom before. This could not be due to local cerebral stimulation nor to any physiological change except one occurring in response to a psycho-social situation. It would seem that, in this instance, it was the way in which the hen jackdaw was regarded by the others which had changed.

A large part of the discussion was summarized by Professor Gerard when he said 'the problem is not how to apply neuro-physiological techniques to the brains of sparrows or cockroaches – this can mostly be done already – but the problem is to know what to look for when you apply them. The whole importance of the new development of the study of animal behaviour in a quantitative, precise and scientific, rather than an anecdotal, manner is that we now do have before us some behavioural patterns that can be observed with a reasonable degree of precision and satisfaction and quantification.'

EXPERIMENTAL NEUROSES IN ANIMALS

Howard S. Liddell

Department of Psychobiology, Cornell University

For some years the focus of interest in our studies of mammalian behaviour has been the comparative anatomy of the stressful environment, and our principal dissecting instruments have been the variants of Pavlov's conditioned reflex method. In every case where conditioning is long enough continued experimental neurosis supervenes.

Our animal subjects are the sheep and the goat. For purposes of disclosing the stressful features of the experimental environment we have found the dog and pig too complex in their behaviour, and the rabbit too simple. Even in the most carefully controlled conditioning experiment the psychosocial situation confronting the animal clearly emerges. In the case of dog and pig the experimenter/animal relationship is of paramount importance. In conditioning, the dog seeks to understand what his master wishes and tries to make his behaviour conform to what is required, even though the stress involved may lead to experimental neurosis. The pig, however, pits his wits against yours, even though this conditioning contest drives him to experimental neurosis.

A much simpler relationship develops between the experimenter and the sheep or goat subject. They come to show a certain degree of confidence in, and dependence upon, him but these emotional bonds are readily relinquished. Except for the brief period of dependence upon the mother in the new-born sheep and goat, loneliness as a psycho-social stress factor does not exist.

A structural feature of the stressful environment in conditioning is loss of freedom due to self-imposed restraint. The experimenter encroaches upon the animal's liberty of action until plasticity and variability of behaviour are replaced by rigidity and stereotypy. The classical Pavlovian conditioning environment with its restraining harness resembles a compression chamber. During training a contest ensues, the animal seeking to discover leaks which the experimenter then contrives to plug up.

Our first case of experimental neurosis in the sheep was observed in 1927 when we were attempting to employ Pavlov's conditioned reflex method in the sheep and goat in order to study the chronic effects of thyroidectomy in these simple farm animals. Stable conditioned reflexes were easily established in both species. At the metronome or buzzer signal the sheep or goat precisely flexes its foreleg. This is followed by a perfunctory, forced flexion to the mild electric shock. The animal then maintains a state of quiet watchfulness in its restraining harness until the next signal.

However, in our zeal to secure data more rapidly, we tripled the number of conditioned reflexes elicited in one of the sheep within three days. This sudden increase in the animal's work load resulted in a dramatic exhibition of diffuse and continuing agitation. It was no longer able to maintain its former pose of tense quiet but showed persistent tic-like movements of the 'trained' foreleg, constant head and ear movement, continual bleating, disturbed breathing, rapid and irregular heart beat with frequent micturition and defecation. A few days' rest only increased its agitation. Its diurnal rhythm of activity became disorganized and it was not quiet at night. Sometimes its hyperactivity approached panic. In the neurotic sheep these manifestations typically persisted for life; i.e. ten to thirteen years. Rest periods up to three years were of no avail.

In the goat we were surprised to discover that the onset of experimental neurosis did not appear with explosive suddenness as in the sheep, but insidiously. Little change in the animal's deportment was observed from day to day, but the subtle changes were cumulative and irreversible. Only after a thousand signals, twenty a day, was the animal's disability clearly apparent to a visitor. This disability, once established, was as permanent and stereotyped as the sheep's diffuse agitation.

The neurosis manifested itself by the following signs. At the signal the goat assumed a rigid posture, the head moved in jerks as if opposed by a stiff spring, and the foreleg was rigidly extended and awkwardly lifted from the platform by a movement at the shoulder. Meanwhile, the heart rate was extraordinarily low for the goat (around sixty per minute) and respiration became progressively more irregular; finally, a series of gasps interrupted by long apnoeic pauses.

In the course of twenty years of investigation we had observed about seventy-five experimentally neurotic sheep and thirty experimentally neurotic goats. These neuroses seemed to affect the life span not at all. Having analysed the manifestations of experimental neurosis in great detail we seemed to be facing a blank wall. Then a heavy door swung slowly on its hinges and we found ourselves in a new room, the animal nursery.

It was due to René Spitz's observations on hospitalism in infants deprived of adequate mothering that our focus of interest shifted to the new-born sheep and goat and the protective functioning of the mother in shielding her young from the impact of psycho-social stress.

The lamb or kid is confined in a room where it is allowed complete freedom of movement. A light cable suspended from the centre of the ceiling is attached to a strap about the animals' chest. Electrodes from this cable are fixed to the foreleg to which a very mild electric shock may be delivered. The cable serves another purpose. Through a system of levers and self-synchronous motors the animal's total pattern of activity for the test hour is recorded in miniature on a chart in an adjoining room. It is also possible to obtain a quantitative estimate of total activity for each conditioning session.

The plan of investigation was simple. We selected sheep and goat mothers with twins of the same sex. One twin was tested in the laboratory room in the presence of its mother, while at the same time the other twin was subjected to an identical training routine in an adjoining room, alone. The same conditioning schedule was followed each day. Since sheep and goats are alarmed by darkness, this has been found to be the most effective conditioning signal for them. The lights in the room were dimmed for ten seconds followed by shock to the foreleg of the lamb or kid. Twenty of these 'darkness' signals spaced two minutes apart and each followed by shock constituted the daily session of about an hour.

In every case, the little animal with its mother showed no restriction of locomotion during the tests. It would run and jump on her at the shock, cuddle up beside her, wander about exploring even though she was lying down and seemingly paying it no attention.

The twin, alone in the adjoining room, soon became immobilized. If the observer were seated in a corner of the room it would face him, cautiously advancing a little, then retreating as if both attracted and repelled by his presence. This behaviour was observed in both lamb and kid.

In these young animals, as training continued, experimental neurosis supervened but pursued a different course from that seen in the adult. In the kid we observed the same rigidity of the forelimb during the conditioned 'darkness' signal as exhibited by the adult neurotic goat.

The lamb, however, first passed through a stage of diffuse agitation with rapidly repeated tic-like movements of the forelimb. But finally it lay down soon after entering the laboratory room, with chin on the floor and made no visible response to the signal, not even ear movement. At the shock it rolled on its side but made no effort to rise.

As already mentioned, with the mother in the room the little animal is seemingly immune to this stress of monotonously recurring apprehension. It seems unperturbed during the two minute waiting periods between signals.

We found that the new-born animals could be conditioned at a very early age, as early as four hours following birth in the lamb or kid. It occurred to us that perhaps the same trauma inflicted upon the young animal by this stressful training in isolation might also be inflicted upon it by interfering with the maternal-neonate relations.

Each of two pregnant goats gave birth to a female kid. These kids, fortunately for our experiment, differed in age by just two days. Karen's mother, at the time of her birth was in a shed with other goats. Their relations following parturition were not experimentally tampered with. Karen is still alive in spite of the stressful training about to be described. The other kid, Jill, was born while her mother was isolated in one of our laboratory rooms. As soon as parturition was complete Jill was licked by her mother for five minutes but then she was taken away to another room for an hour, at the end of which the mother rejoined her. But they could not establish normal relations even with our assistance in helping the kid in nursing. So Jill never had adequate mothering. The mother really paid her no attention and did not protect her duing play as successful goat mothers always do.

When they were seven weeks of age Karen and Jill were subjected to the stressful conditioning routine in the absence of the mother previously described. We had been plotting their growth curves since birth. From the start the two curves sharply diverged with Jill lagging behind in weight increase. As soon as the period of stressful conditioning began, however, the growth of both kids was arrested and the growth curves flattened to plateaux. Then training was discontinued and both goats were left free in the pasture except for periodic weighing. At once both curves started upward again. A second period of training brought even more pronounced arrest of growth. When conditioning was again discontinued the growth curves once more began to rise. Three more periods of training followed separated by brief rest periods of two or three weeks. The inhibitory effect on growth was progressively greater as we continued. Karen's growth was definitely retarded by these later periods of training but Jill's was absolutely arrested. During the final conditioning session Jill progressively lost weight and soon died. Karen kept on increasing in weight and is now a mature, healthy goat.

Jill and Karen at one year and three months of age each gave birth to a male offspring; again, fortunately for the purposes of our investigation, only a day apart in age. We named Karen's kid Kelly, and Jill's kid Jerry. Karen behaved as a normal mother. Although she had been subjected to the stresses of conditioning in isolation she had nevertheless the benefits of normal maternal protection outside of the laboratory. Jerry was born just a few months before the death of his mother, Jill. She proved to be as ineffective a mother as her own mother had been (presumably because of our separation of Jill and her mother for an hour shortly after birth). Thus we were in the position of being able to study two generations of defective maternal/neonate relations.

At three months of age Kelly and Jerry were transferred to a summer pasture for three months with other young males, but no females. As soon as they were returned to our flock at the end of the summer the behaviour of Kelly and Jerry differed conspicuously. Kelly pursued the females, mounting them one after another. Jerry, on the other hand, exhibited complete indifference to them, remaining composed and withdrawn from the rest of the flock. He died at a year and three months of age. At autopsy his testes were found to be atrophic and he was parasite-ridden. Although all of our sheep and goats are periodically wormed and receive the best veterinary attention the animals subjected to long continued conditioning seem to be particularly subject to infestation by the parasites common to these grazing animals. By contrast, Kelly with the benefits of adequate maternal care is still living and in good health.

In passing, it should be noted that in our flocks of sheep and goats the laboratory trained animals are not separated from the others in the pasture. This intermingling facilitates our study of the social behaviour of the sheep and goats which have been subjected to stress.

We began conditioning Kelly and Jerry at nine months of age. They were subjected to our standard one hour routine of twenty conditioned signals always followed by shock and spaced two minutes apart.

The growth curves of Jerry and Kelly follow the same pattern that we have already seen in the growth curves of their mothers. Kelly gained in weight while Jerry lagged behind. The first period of conditioning sessions caused a much more pronounced inhibition of growth in Jerry than in Kelly. Then, as in the case of their mothers, during a vacation period growth increased but during a second period of conditioning Jerry definitely went down hill. With a further rest period of several weeks Kelly continued to gain in weight but Jerry made no progress. During a third and final training period both goats showed a marked loss of weight. At the end of this stressful period, however, Jerry never recovered and soon had to be sent to the veterinary clinic where he shortly died.

The effect of this stressful training — that is the monotonous schedule of repeated darkness signals to which the young animal is subjected in the absence of its mother when it is from three weeks to three months of age — on later pregnancy and early post partum care of the young is quite interesting. Nearly ninety per cent. of our ewes subjected to early conditioning abort or lose their lambs within a few days in their first three pregnancies. In a smaller number of goats we have observed that about sixty per cent. abort during the first pregnancy. Goats seem more resistant than sheep to the effects of early conditioning on later pregnancy. But for both sheep and goats without such early stressful training, less than ten per cent. abort or lose their young within the first few days.

However, the period of greatest vulnerability to the stresses of conditioning is from four hours to three weeks of age when the animal is deprived of the mother's presence in the experimental room. It is as if she serves as a *security signal* indicating that all is well.

We trained ten kids in isolation at four to fourteen hours of age *for just one session of about an hour* with twenty signals at two minute intervals. Of the ten subjected to this early conditioning, two had died within a week and haemorrhagic adrenal cortices were discovered at autopsy. All but one of the remaining eight died in the summer pasture at less than a year of age. So only one out of these ten survived.

We also conditioned ten pairs of twin kids at about one month of age. Five of these twins were trained alone and five with the mother. Four of the five that were trained in isolation died within the year, while only one of the five trained in the presence of the mother died within the year.

Our last result shows that the separation from mother is more important, however, than the conditioning: we tried the effect of simply removing the kid from its mother. We had under observation twenty-two control kids in which there was no separation from the mother following parturition and for comparison twenty-one experimental kids separated from the mother five minutes following birth and kept away from her, alone in an adjoining room, for half an hour to two hours. Now nineteen of the twenty-one experimental kids separated from the mother had died in the summer pasture at less than a year of age, but only two of the twenty-two control kids died that summer. None of these forty-three kids were subjected to any form of conditioning or training.

SUMMARY

In view of the experimental findings presented here it is necessary to broaden our conception of Pavlovian conditioning. Prolonged conditioning in the adult sheep or goat inevitably results in neurotic illness which does not shorten the normal life span of ten to thirteen years. However, in the lamb or kid still dependent upon the mother conditioning in isolation typically results in death within a year. But separation from the mother for an hour following birth also commonly results in the death of the lamb or kid at an early age. Hence, we must further broaden our conception of conditioning to include *mutual conditioning* between mother and new-born by which the mother's presence becomes a conditioned *security signal* to her offspring. This mutual conditioning establishes a stable pleasure organization between mother and newborn which promotes its healthy growth and development.

CHAPTER 4

PHYSIOLOGICAL RESPONSES TO STRESSORS

THE CONCEPT OF STRESS IN EXPERIMENTAL PHYSIOLOGY

HANS SELYE[1]

Institute of Experimental Medicine and Surgery, University of Montreal

Since the description, in 1936, of the general adaptation syndrome (the body's response to nonspecific stress), numerous investigations have been published throughout the world, in an attempt to clarify the mechanism through which, depending upon circumstances, stress can either produce, or prevent, disease (Selye, 1950-55/6). More particularly, it has been the major endeavour of our Institute to prove that hormones can play a decisive role in the development of several nonendocrine diseases, that is, of maladies which are not primarily due to derangements originating in the endocrine glands themselves.

During the last twenty years, it has been amply demonstrated that, in response to a variety of stressors (trauma, infections, intoxications, nervous stimuli, etc.), the body reacts in a rather stereotyped manner, by the secretion of certain hormones, such as adrenocorticotrophic hormone (ACTH) and corticoids. The resulting excess in these 'adaptive hormones' is an essentially useful defence reaction. However under certain circumstances, it can become the cause of disease or, at least, predispose the body to the production of morbid changes. For example, the excessive secretion of ACTH and of anti-inflammatory corticoids is useful, because it helps the body to survive during an emergency and because it suppresses excessive inflammatory reactions; but, at the same time, it can also be harmful in that it may enhance the spread of infections or predispose to the production of peptic ulcers.

The major results of our investigations were subsequently summarized in a monograph for the general public (Selye, 1956), so that I shall limit myself here to a re-assessment of the concept of stress and diseases of adaption, with a brief reference to some of the key experiments upon which the concept is based and, particularly, to our latest findings on the prevention of stress-induced myocardial necroses.

[1] The experimental work on which this article is based was performed with the aid of a Consolidated Grant from the National Research Council of Canada as well as of grants from the Lilly Research Laboratories and the Pfizer Laboratories.

Stress, like health, disease, or life itself, is difficult to define in precise terms. We have attempted elsewhere (Selye, 1956) to formulate a rather precise definition but, for practical purposes, it will suffice to say that *stress is the consequence of the rate of wear and tear in a biological system.* This 'system' may be the organism as a whole (systemic stress) or one of its parts (topical stress). The visible manifestations of the former constitute the 'General Adaptation Syndrome (G.A.S.)', while those of the latter are known as the 'Local Adaptation Syndrome (L.A.S.)'. The G.A.S., like the L.A.S., is a triphasic reaction which evolves through an acute phase, the 'alarm reaction', to the 'stage of resistance' and finally ends in the 'stage of exhaustion' (see Fig. 3). In the case

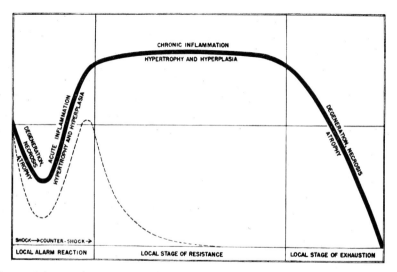

Fig. 3.—Schematic drawing illustrating the characteristic changes in morphologic structure and topical resistance, as they occur during the three stages of the L.A.S. The heavy line represents 'specific resistance', the interrupted line 'crossed resistance'. (After Selye and co-workers, 1950).

of the G.A.S. the manifestations of these three stages are systemic, that is, not limited to the primarily affected area of the body. Thus, after a localized burn, the reaction spreads throughout the body: there is stimulation of the hypothalamus, increased ACTH and corticoid secretion, etc. (Fig. 4). All of these are remote consequences of the local stress situation. It is particularly striking that these manifold systemic manifestations are largely independent of the specific nature of the 'stressor' (trauma, infection, X-rays, nervous stimuli) that induces the stress situation. In the primarily affected area itself we also note a triphasic nonspecific reaction, but its manifestations (cell proliferation, inflammation, necroses) are limited to that region of the body which is directly influenced by the stressor.

Since stress is a general manifestation of vital activity, it has often been confused with somewhat related but essentially different aspects of life from which it must be strictly distinguished.

Any kind of physiologic activity (locomotion, heart beat, respiration, glandular secretion) produces some wear-and-tear. Complete freedom from stress never occurs in living beings; hence, *stress is not necessarily a pathologic phenomenon.*

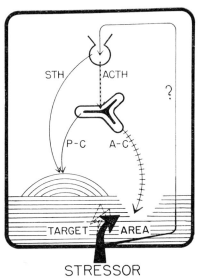

FIG. 4.—Schema of the principal pathway of nonspecific or stressor effects. The stressor acts upon the target (the body or some part of it) directly (thick arrow) and indirectly through the pituitary and adrenal glands. Through some unknown pathway (question mark), the first mediator travels from the directly injured target area to the anterior pituitary. It notifies the latter that a condition of stress exists and thus induces it to discharge ACTH. (ACs = antiphlogistic, or glucocorticoids (GCs); PCs = prophlogistic, or mineralocorticoids (MCs). (After Selye, 1952.)

Soon after the discovery of the '*alarm reaction*' as a stereotyped response to nonspecific stress, it was noted that the principal manifestations of this re-action that were known at that time (adrenal hyperplasia with signs of hyper-activity, thymicolymphatic involution and eosinopenia, gastro-intestinal ulcers) tended to disappear after a few days, even if the organism continued to be exposed to the same degree of the same stressor agents ('*stage of resist-ance*'). Eventually, if the stressor is sufficiently severe, the '*stage of exhaustion*' ensues.

6

The striking hyperplasia and hyperactivity of the adrenal cortex represented a clue for a series of experiments designed to explore the value of corticoids in the body's *resistance* to potentially pathogenic agents. It was found that although both glucocorticoids and mineralocorticoids can prolong the life of adrenalectomized animals, the former are much more effective than the latter in raising resistance to stressors (e.g., trauma, haemorrhage, toxic chemicals).

Although only very intense overdosage with corticoids produces manifestations of disease, even small amounts of these hormones can decisively influence the effects of certain nonhormonal pathogens. For example, the *experimental arthritis* produced by the injection of formalin into the paw of a rat can be prevented by relatively small doses of glucocorticoids and aggravated by mineralocorticoids.

The so-called '*anaphylactoid inflammation*' that ensues in rats, following the intraperitoneal or intravenous administration of egg-white, dextran and other macromolecular substances, is similarly influenced by the same types of hormones. Both the antiphlogistic effects of glucocorticoids and the prophlogistic actions of mineralocorticoids are more evident in the adrenalectomized than in the intact animal, presumably because, in the latter, endogenous corticoids of the opposite type can interfere with the actions of the hormones that are injected.

Further investigations showed that heavy overdosage with mineralocorticoids (e.g., desoxycorticosterone) can, under certain conditions, produce a simile of the so-called *collagen diseases* in animals. For example, using desoxycorticosterone it is possible to induce nephrosclerosis with hypertension, periarteritis nodosa and a myocarditis with intense hyalinization; but the development of this syndrome depends upon certain '*conditioning factors*'.

Although hormones play a prominent role in the G.A.S., stress-induced derangements of non-endocrine organs (e.g., nervous system, liver, kidney) may also cause diseases of adaptation.

For instance, in rats heavily overdosed with desoxycorticosterone (especially if they are sensitized by a high sodium chloride intake and unilateral nephrectomy) there develops an encephalopathy with periarteritis nodosa of the cerebral vessels, marked edema, and often multiple massive haemorrhages in the brain. These lesions are accompanied by convulsions or paralytic changes in the skeletal musculature and by an extreme irritability of the animals. It is possible to prevent such changes by the administration of acidifying salts, for instance, ammonium chloride or calcium chloride.

The question arises as to whether cerebral changes, such as are seen in clinical periarteritis nodosa and in hypertensive disease, are related to the excessive production of mineralocorticoids or an excessive conditioning for their actions. In any event, this experimental encephalopathy now serves as a useful test object for the screening of drugs that may have clinical applications in those diseases of man simulated by desoxycorticosterone overdosage.

Many other diseases could be cited as examples in which maladaptation, in the form of inadequate hormone secretion, plays a decisive role. Here I would only like to mention one more disease of this type, because it represented the major research problem of our Institute during the last two years, and to my mind is the most promising aspect of our stress research, because of its probable clinical applicability. I refer to *the fatal heart accident* which is one of the most common and dramatic causes of death in man.

Ever since our first studies on stress, we have wanted to explore the mechanism of this condition with a view of finding some remedy against it. It is well known from clinical experience that sudden cardiac death occurs most frequently after some acute exposure to stress, such as intense muscular effort or nervous excitement. However, in order to analyse the mechanism of a disease, it is essential first to reproduce a simile of it in experimental animals, so that potentially dangerous treatments may be tested. This was not possible as regards the fatal heart accident, because even if animals are killed by stress, they die from reasons other than the so-called acute cardiac infarcts or necrosis. Recently, however, we succeeded in clarifying the conditions under which stress will regularly produce such sudden heart accidents in experimental animals (Selye, 1958).

If rats, rabbits, dogs or monkeys are pretreated with certain corticoids and sodium salts, they do not develop a heart accident, but if following this sensitization or 'conditioning', the animals are subsequently exposed to stressors (for example, hot or cold baths, surgical injuries, forced muscular exercise or restraint), they regularly develop acute heart accidents owing to the death (that is, necrosis) of portions of their cardiac muscle. Using this test object, it was possible to show that potassium chloride and magnesium chloride offer certain protection against this type of cardiac death in animals. It remains to be seen whether the results of these animal experiments are applicable to the prophylaxis of cardiac death in man; only few clinical observations have been made as yet about this possible new preventive treatment, but these are rather encouraging.

The experiments just mentioned led to the concept that some diseases that are not primarily due to an increased or insufficient corticoid secretion may, in the final analysis, nevertheless be due to hypo- or hypercorticoidism, respectively. For example, a decreased resistance to infections may be viewed as due to an increase in glucocorticoids (e.g., during stress), since overdosage with ACTH and cortisone does, in fact, diminish resistance to infections in experimental animals. Conversely, a diminished activity of prophlogistic hormones (e.g., STH) may have the same effect, as judged by the observation that injections of STH are highly effective in restoring towards normal the decreased resistance to infection that can be induced by antiphlogistic hormones. Furthermore, acute gastric ulcers—such as are characteristic of the alarm reaction—can be produced with an excess of glucocorticoids both in experimental animals and in man. This suggested the possibility that spontaneous gastroduodenal ulcers may likewise partly depend upon an increased antiphlogistic hormone activity. If this concept is correct, we shall have to consider certain maladies that tend to develop during stress as 'diseases of adaptation', maladies which are not only due to the actions of the apparent pathogen, but largely also to changes in disease susceptibility induced by inadequate hormonal reactions to stress.

In the supposed diseases of adaptation of man, marked changes in the blood level or urinary elimination of hormones can rarely be observed. This fact led to the conclusion that endocrine factors do not play a decisive role in the pathogenesis of such maladies.

However, the theory of the diseases of adaptation does not postulate an *absolute* increase or decrease in hormone production, but rather a change in hormone activity. The latter may be due to faulty conditioning, and hence, need not be reflected by any absolute change in hormone levels. Thus, a nearly 'normal' glucocorticoid secretion, such as suffices to maintain homeostasis at rest, is grossly insufficient to maintain the life of an adrenalectomized animal exposed to stress. Such a 'normal' secretion also fails to prevent inflammation in the presence of a special irritant (e.g., formalin, in the case of the experimental arthritis, or egg-white, in the case of the anaphylactoid inflammation). Here, the pathogenic factor would be precisely the maintenance of the normal hormone level when the situation calls for a considerable increase. Conversely, as we have seen, in themselves well tolerated amounts of desoxycorticosterone or STH can acquire severe pathogenic potencies, owing to changes in the metabolic conditioning factors which determine susceptibility to their toxic effects. Therefore, an increase in corticoid activity must not be equated with an increase in corticoid hormone secretion.

It was thought, furthermore, that *if stress and the stress hormones were responsible for the development of the various diseases of adaptation, these should all be present simultaneously*, whenever an individual is exposed to stress. This is not the case and, indeed, it was not to be expected in view of what we have just said about selective conditioning. Dietary factors, interference with the normal function of an organ, hereditary predisposition and many other factors can selectively increase or decrease the responsiveness of individual organs to the potentially pathogenic actions of stress or stress hormones. In the light of what we know about the widely different manifestations of infections with the same micro-organism (e.g., tuberculosis of the lungs, skin, bones, miliary tuberculosis), it is not unexpected that exposure to the same stressor may affect various individuals in essentially distinct ways.

It has also been thought that *overdosage with a hormone, be it relative (e.g., owing to special conditioning) or absolute, should invariably be accompanied by clinical manifestations characteristic of an excess in this endocrine principle.* This is likewise not a valid assumption. For example, in rats kept on *Lathyrus odoratus* seeds and treated with small amounts of STH, the 'growth hormone' produces pronounced skeletal and joint deformities, yet it fails to stimulate growth. Apparently, the active principle in these seeds simultaneously sensitizes to the pathogenic actions and desensitizes to the normal physiologic growth effect of STH.

The fact that stress — no matter how produced — elicits a rather stereo-type nonspecific response, the G.A.S., has now been established with certainty. It is also clear that at least some manifestations of the G.A.S. do possess a defensive value, i.e., they facilitate adaptation to various stressors. We have learned, furthermore, that by suitable humoral conditioning disease susceptibility can be markedly altered; not only is it possible to increase or decrease resistance to stress (e.g., influence survival but we can selectively direct the effect of stress against a certain organ (e.g., produce selective cardiac necroses by a cold bath).

Outlook

I have attempted to discuss some much disputed aspects of stress and the diseases of adaptation, as well as certain novel facets of stress research which, we hope, will open new avenues in the study of cardiovascular pathology. But, actually, the questions raised here led us beyond the limits of what we currently consider typical stress research. This broader horizon was barely visible a decade ago, when I last attempted to survey it in a series of lectures subsequently printed in 1952. But the leitmotiv which prefaced this booklet is perhaps better supported by facts today than it was when I first had the temerity to assert what was then assailed by so many as rank heresy, namely that:

'Now the great problem in endocrine physiology is no longer "what do the hormones do?" but what *adaptive reactions do they influence*? Now the great problem in endocrine pathology is no longer "which diseases are caused by the excessive function or the destruction of an endocrine gland?" but *in which diseases has the endocrine status a decisive influence*?

'Indeed, even apart from endocrinology, the principal endeavor of medicine in general is beginning to change. It is no longer the search for specific pathogens, and for specific remedies with which to eradicate them. We always used to accept as a self-evident fact that each well-characterized individual disease must have its own specific cause. This tenet is self-evident no longer. It becomes increasingly more manifest that an agent does or does not produce disease, depending upon a variety of conditions, some of which have now been definitely identified as being determined by the "adaptive hormones".

'There begins to emerge a new and somewhat more complex pathology in which *the main objects of our study are no longer individual "pathogens", but rather "pathogenic situations".*'

DISCUSSION

Dr Lacey described some results obtained in a longitudinal study of children at the Fels Institute. Children were subjected to a number of noxious stimuli such as the cold pressor test and their pattern of autonomic response was recorded. Individuals differed greatly in this pattern; one would react with a large digital vaso-constriction but little else, while another would react with a marked temporary elevation of systolic blood pressure with little change in skin resistance or blood flow.

The pattern of response of a group of children studied at the age of six and restudied at the age of ten, was remarkably constant from one age to another. It seemed that already by the age of six, if not earlier, a constitutional organ vulnerability had appeared.

Further than this he had found that the same patterns were produced by a range of stressors. The individual may be hyperventilated, subjected to the cold pressor test or made to do mental arithmetic, and although the quantity of his response may differ in these situations, the pattern of response tends to remain the same. Individuals can be ranged on a scale of stereotypy – that is, constancy in their pattern of response to these various stimuli – and it was interesting to speculate that persons prone to develop psychosomatic disorders may be those who earlier in life show the highest degree of stereotypy. Thus, the distribution of strain is uneven within the organism and conditioned, apparently, by the organism's heredity and past history.

Professor Selye stressed that these organ system predispositions, often regarded in man as constitutional, could nevertheless be produced by experimental procedures in animals. If an animal was prepared in different ways then stress could produce such different patterns as bone lathyrism, periarteritis nodosum, tuberculosis, or death from saprophytosis. In the same animal prepared in the same manner, the same agent however, will always produce the same response. Dr Tanner pointed out that this was essentially the production of phenocopies of constitutional disease predispositions.

Dr Lacey added that there were certain manipulations that could alter the pattern of autonomic response. This could be done by changing the demand made on the organism. This was one of the reasons why he objected to the notion that autonomic responses such as are obtained with noxious stimulation were simply inappropriate in amount. Autonomic responses were not just atavistic survivals occurring primarily in response to noxious stimuli. Recent research had shown that in reality they were instrumental acts of the organism used in controlling skeletal motor behaviour. By a historical accident the visceral afferents were arbitrarily excluded from textbook definitions of the autonomic nervous system. But it was through the visceral afferents and not the sensory afferents that autonomic discharges were fed back to the central nervous system and there exerted their behaviour and perhaps behavioural disorganization.

SOME ENDOCRINE STRESS RESPONSES IN MAN

Hudson Hoagland

Worcester Foundation for Experimental Biology, Shrewsbury, Massachusetts

Stress may be considered as any set of events which modify steady state conditions within the organism so as to activate homeostatic processes to adjust the internal environment. Thus a shift in blood acidity following exercise calls upon both chemical buffering systems and neurophysiological mechanisms to re-establish homeostasis. External temperature changes activate autonomic regulatory mechanisms to maintain constancy of temperature of the internal environment. The ingestion of chemical agents, foodstuffs in excess, or noxious agents likewise activate homeostatic processes and all of these events may be considered as stressful as they are reflected in measures of homeostatic adjustment.

Stress has a broader meaning for the organism in relation to its external environment. Any external situation threatening the organism may function as a stress. Thus activities of flight and fight with their concomitant psychological and physiological expressions of fear and anger are stressful. The processes of inhibiting fight and flight may result in stressful anxiety states. Psychological stress results from the intensification of instinctual drives and of the control of these drives to meet the demands of society. Such stresses may be chronic and produce far-reaching disturbances of a psychosomatic nature. The balancing of one's needs and satisfaction in terms of conscience represent stresses of this sort. The apparently same psychological stress situation may have quite different meanings for different persons in terms of their life histories and past conditionings so that attempts to objectify and standardize such stresses meet with great difficulty.

For the purposes of this discussion, I would like to limit considerations to responses of the adrenal cortex and adrenal medulla in man when stressed both by life situations and by experimental procedures in the laboratory which may call upon these endocrine systems to increase their outputs of hormones as measured by metabolic indices in the urine.

The studies to be reported deal primarily with investigations of our group at the Worcester Foundation and are concerned with responses of men to challenging situations both of a psychological and physiological nature.

Since 1943 we have published a number of papers dealing with stress responses of the adrenal systems in normal men and in mental patients. I would like first to review some studies of my colleague Dr Fred Elmadjian who in association with Dr Justin Hope and Mr Edwin Lamson has investigated the urinary excretion of epinephrine and norepinephrine in stressed individuals (Elmadjian, Hope and Lamson, 1957; 1958). Elmadjian and his collaborators obtained data from normal subjects engaged in professional hockey playing and also from amateur boxers before and after fights. They also studied the excretion of epinephrine (E) and norepinephrine (NE) in psychiatric patients appearing at staff conferences. In addition they correlated data on E and NE

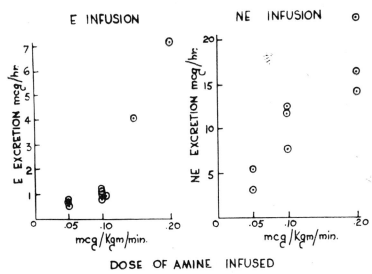

FIG. 5.—The excretion of epinephrine (E) and norepinephrine (NE) above control levels after thirty-minute infusion of E and NE in doses of 0·05, 0·10 and 0·20 μg./Kg./min. (see text).

excretion with a measure of hostility in a group of patients and finally obtained data on both therapist and patient during psychotherapeutic interviews.

From these studies will emerge the view that active aggressive, hostile behavior is accompanied primarily by the enhancement of NE excretion while anxious passive behavior primarily results in enhanced E excretion.

Appropriately timed urine samples collected before a stress and again after the stress were extracted by the alumina absorption method of von Euler and Hellner (von Euler and Hellner, 1951). The maximum efficiency of this method yields sixty to seventy per cent. of the catechol amines based on recovery data. Bioassays on the extracts were performed by a modification of the method described by Gaddum and Lembeck (1949). This consists of testing the sample on the rat colon for NE and the rat uterus for E. The bioassay is based on the quantitative inhibition by the catechol amines of the contractions induced in vitro in a 2-ml. bath with acetylcholine. The inhibitions of NE and E are approximately equal when tested on the colon; but when tested on the uterus, E is 75 to 300 times more potent than NE. The colon assay was used when rapid estimates of total (NE + E) were desired.

To calibrate extraction and bioassay data in terms of E and NE excretion, Elmadjian carried out infusion experiments. Fig. 5 depicts the data of ten E infusions and nine NE infusions at rates of dosage of 0·05, 0·10, and 0·20 μg/kgm/min. Pre-infusion urine was collected from 9.0 a.m. to 10.0 a.m. at which time the infusion was started and continued for thirty minutes. The infusion collection represented urine collection ranging from 10.0 a.m. to approximately 11.0 a.m. The data in Fig. 5 presents the hourly excretion for each dosage rate above its control collection. In the case of E, only 0·5–1·0 per cent. of the total dose infused appears in the urine, while in the case of NE from 3·0–5·0 per cent. of the total dose is excreted in excess of the control sample. In the NE infusions the relationship of excretion rate to dosage is essentially linear. However, in the case of E infusion, there is a sharp change in the slope at doses above 0·10 μg/kgm/min. While there is a two-fold increase in the excretion rate with the doubling of the dose from 0·05 to 0·10 μg/kgm/min. there is a seven-fold increase in the excretion rate on subsequent doubling from 0·10 to 0·20 μg/kgm/min. These data serve as a basis for estimating the approximate secretion rate of E and NE in the studies to be reported.

TABLE 13

DIURNAL VARIATION OF NOREPINEPHRINE (NE) AND EPINEPHRINE (E)
EXCRETION IN NORMAL SUBJECTS[1]

Sample period[2]	NE (μg./hr.)	E (μg./hr.)
	Study A (ten subjects)	
Sleep	1·2	0·02
	±0·12	±0·002
Morning . . .	2·9	0·40
	±0·48	±0·10
	Study B (six subjects)	
Sleep	1·2	0·02
	±0·14	±0·01
Morning . . .	2·3	0·10
	±0·49	±0·02
Day	2·4	0·21
	±0·60	±0·07

[1] From Elmadjian et al. (1958).
[2] See text for times of collection.

Studies of E and NE excretion showed marked diurnal rhythms. Table 13 presents data on the NE and E excretion during sleep and waking states on ten normal subjects. Night samples of urine were collected during a period from approximately 10.0 p.m. to 6.30 a.m. and morning samples from 6.30 to noon. All subjects had breakfast and conducted their usual activities consisting of laboratory routines. Table 13 contains additional data on six normal subjects consisting of physicians and laboratory personnel who were conducting their usual daily activities. Each collected a sample representing the period of sleeping; a second sample from the time of waking to about 10.0 a.m. and a third sample from 10.0 a.m. to the time of retiring at night. There is seen a marked increase in the excretion rate of both E and NE during morning and day samples over that observed during sleep. The NE increases were smaller percentagewise than values for E. For future reference we may note that morning and afternoon samples of E excretion have values ranging from approximately 0·1 to 0·4 μg/hr per person; while NE values are from 2·0 to 3·0 μg/hr.

Studies of Athletes

TABLE 14

EXCRETION OF NOREPINEPHRINE (NE) AND EPINEPHRINE (E) IN MEMBERS OF A PROFESSIONAL HOCKEY TEAM—DEFENSEMEN AND FORWARDS VERSUS NONPARTICIPATING PLAYERS[1]

Urine Collection	Number of Hockey Players Sampled	NE (μg./100 mg. Creatinine)	E (μg./100 mg. Creatinine)
Active hockey players (defensemen and forwards)[2]			
Pregame	20	2·7±0·43	0·36±0·07
Postgame	20	15·3±2·20	0·95±0·21
		$t = 5·66$	$t = 2·68$
		$P = <0·001$	$P = <0·05, >0·01$
Two players who did not participate in the game[3]			
Pregame	1 (No. 18)	2·2	0·23
Postgame		3·3	0·75
Pregame	1 (No. 10)	5·6	0·78
Postgame		5·3	1·42
Player involved in fist fight			
Pregame	1 (No. 16)	3·5	0·18
Postgame		29·3	3·30

[1] From Elmadjian et al. (1958).
[2] The approximate hourly excretion is 10 per cent. less than the figure given in terms of 100 gm. creatinine when corrected by creatinine coefficient.
[3] Due to their physical condition.

Hockey is a fast aggressive game involving vigorous attack and defense. Studies were made of players on a high grade professional team, the Boston Bruins. Timed pre-game samples of urine were collected at ten to thirty minutes before game time, which was 8.30 p.m. and timed post-game samples were collected some three hours later. These latter samples included urine formed during the contest. Results from a number of games were studied. Table 14 lists values for pre-game and post-game collections of the aggressive defensemen and forwards who do most of the skating. The data are presented in terms of creatinine values because it was not always possible to obtain properly timed samples. For samples taken following the game, there was a six-fold increase in NE excretion. Two players were sampled before the game, but on physical examination by the trainer, they were not permitted to participate. In the same table are presented the data on these players, indicating no post-game increase in NE but appreciable increase in E. Both players sat on the bench and watched the game. Both were concerned about their injuries and inability to play.

In Table 14 are also data on a player No. 16 who showed a nine-fold increase in NE and a twenty-fold increase in E. He skated his regular turn, but did not play an outstanding game. At the end of the second period however, he got involved in a violent fist fight with an opposing player and was ejected from the game.

TABLE 15

EXCRETION OF NE AND E IN PROFESSIONAL HOCKEY PLAYERS—GOAL TENDER AND COACH

	Number of Samples		Urine Collection		NE (μg./100 mg. Creatinine)		E (μg./100 mg. Creatinine)
Goal tender . .	3	.	Pre-game	.	$3 \cdot 3 \pm 0 \cdot 7$	.	$0 \cdot 45 \pm 0 \cdot 20$
			Post-game	.	$9 \cdot 2 \pm 1 \cdot 8$	.	$1 \cdot 30 \pm 0 \cdot 81$
Coach . . .	6	.	Pre-game	.	$1 \cdot 8 \pm 0 \cdot 5$	.	$0 \cdot 38 \pm 0 \cdot 09$
			Post-game	.	$3 \cdot 7 \pm 0 \cdot 9$	.	$0 \cdot 43 \pm 0 \cdot 21$

For discussion see text.   From Elmadjian *et al.* (1957).

The goal tender skates very little but is in constant vigilance in front of the net ready to defend the goal. The coach remains on the bench directing strategy. Data obtained on the goal tender in three games and on the coach in six games are presented in Table 15. There was a marked increase in both E and NE excretion in the goal tender but on the average there were no significant changes in the excretion of either amine in the coach. There were, however, individual games where the coach showed marked increase in E.

Another study was made on six amateur boxers competing in the finals of the Amateur Athletic Union boxing championship. Especial significance was placed on these three-round finals because the winners would thereby qualify for the final Olympic tryouts. A high state of expectancy characterized the fighters. This was reflected in the elevated E excretion rates observed in most of the pre-fight samples seen in Table 16.

TABLE 16

EXCRETION OF NE AND E IN AMATEUR BOXERS

Boxer	Urine Collection	NE (μg./100 mg. Creatinine)	E (μg./100 mg. Creatinine)
Ch . . .	Pre-contest .	17·9	1·64
	Post-contest .	—	—
Sm . . .	Pre-contest .	38·1	1·78
	Post-contest .	32·4	0·67
Br . . .	Pre-contest .	4·2	0·40
	Post-contest .	7·0	0·87
Pe · · ·	Pre-contest .	6·7	0·22
	Post-contest .	2·8	0·41
Why . . .	Pre-contest .	1·7	1·67
	Post-contest .	—	—
Bra . . .	Pre-contest .	—	—
	Post-contest .	15·9	1·70

From Elmadjian et al. (1957).

On three fighters only one sample was obtained; on Ch and Why the sample was a pre-contest collection. Both boxers showed elevated E excretion. Each showed ample evidence of tenseness and apprehension in the pre-fight interview. After the interview Ch went to the corner of the dressing room and shadow boxed for about five minutes, while Wh sat quietly on a bench with his trainer and refrained from shadow boxing before entering the ring. Ch who shadow boxed showed an elevated NE excretion while Wh's NE value was low.

In general high NE pre-fight values were noted in fighters who engaged in vigorous shadow boxing before the contest. The highest pre-fight E excretions were found in the fighters who showed the greater degree of anticipation preceding the fight. Increase in the post-fight samples over the pre-fight samples of E were observed in those fighters who had to fight the distance for decision in close contests.

Studies of Neuropsychiatric Patients

In ten psychiatric patients a study was made of the relationship between certain scores of the Malamud-Sands rating scale (Malamud, Hope and Elmadjian, 1951) and the excretions of E and NE. This scale rates the patient numerically in a number of categories. In comparing behavior characteristics with NE excretion gradations of motor activity and gradations of hostility reactions were used and a composite score including only these two items of the Malamud-Sands ratings. Fig. 6 shows the relationship of this score to NE excretion. Patients with active, aggressive emotional display have higher NE excretion while those with passive self-effacing emotional display had normal levels of NE. In this figure when a line appears through the circles, it indicates that these subjects also had a high excretion of E. The subject indicated by an asterisk had normal NE excretion, but the excretion of E was 2·75 μg. per hour which is extremely high. This subject showed periodic bursts of escitement with expressions of fear and guilt.

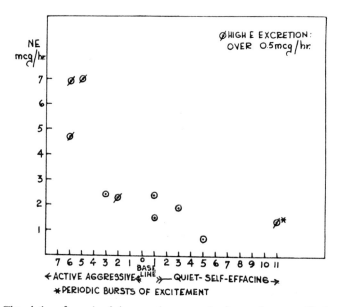

FIG. 6.—The relation of norepinephrine excretion to emotional state of neuropsychiatric patients. (The abscissa depicts the composite score for the functions of motor activity and hostility reactions from the Malamud-Sands rating scale, and the ordinate represents the excretion of norepinephrine in μg. per hour during the observation period.)

Studies also were made of neuropsychiatric patients during staff interviews. The patients are seated and are questioned by a psychiatrist before some twenty members of the hospital medical staff. The patient is aware that decisions about his continued stay in hospital will emerge from the interview. Eleven patients were studied by Elmadjian et al. on eight of whom control samples were obtained. The interviews took place in the mornings and the control samples were obtained at the same time on the next day. The results are shown in Table 17. There were no changes in NE excretion when the interview day was compared with the control. However, in every subject on whom a control was obtained there was an elevated excretion of E during the interview. As might be expected there were marked individual variations in this increase. The subjects in general were self-effacing and on their best behaviour and showed no aggressive or active emotional display.

TABLE 17

EXCRETION OF NE AND E DURING STAFF CONFERENCE INTERVIEW OF 11 NEUROPSYCHIATRIC PATIENTS

	Number of Samples	NE (μg./hr.)	E (μg./hr.)
Interview day . .	11	. 2·6±0·4	. 0·50±0·14
Control day . .	8	. 2·3±0·2	. 0·27±0·12
			P = less than 0·001

From Elmadjian et al. (1957).

In another study urine samples were obtained from therapist and patient in a series of psychotherapeutic interviews carried on between 8.0 a.m. and 9.0 a.m. Samples were obtained before and after each therapeutic session as well as on control days during the same hours when neither subject was involved in a psychotherapeutic interview. Six psychotherapeutic sessions and six control days were studied. Urine samples were analysed for NE, E and 17-hydroxy-corticosteroids. Fig. 7 shows data on both therapist and patient. Along the abscissa are indicated the control values for both therapist and patient. Elmadjian, Hope and Lamson (1958) have described these results as follows: 'During the interview we observe that both patient and therapist showed normal values during the first psychotherapeutic session as compared to their control values. In the second session a slight elevation is observed in the NE and 17-hydroxycorticosteroid excretion for the therapist with the patient still within normal limits for these determinations. In the third session the results indicate that all values are within normal limits. In the fourth psychotherapeutic interview, the samples indicated a two-fold increase in the 17-hydroxycorticosteroid excretion with marked elevations for both E and NE for the therapist. The patient still showed normal values. In the fifth psychotherapeutic session we observed elevated 17-hydroxycorticosteroid values for the therapist accompanied by high values in NE, but E values were normal. However, we now observe the patient showing a marked increase in NE excretion with considerable elevation in E excretion (especially for this patient) with no increase in 17-hydroxycorticosteroid excretion. In the sixth interview we note again a highly elevated 17-hydroxycorticosteroid excretion for the therapist with a moderately high NE value and normal E excretion. The patient's values show an elevated NE, but E is back to normal.

Information obtained from the therapist indicated that in session number 4 the therapist was severely criticized by the patient and the interview got 'out of hand'. The therapist was aware of his predicament subjectively and did admit unpleasant emotional experience. In the fifth session during the course of the psychotherapeutic interview the patient cried, showing considerable emotional expression. The therapist was quite concerned about the turn of events which had now taken an unexpected course for the worse with regard

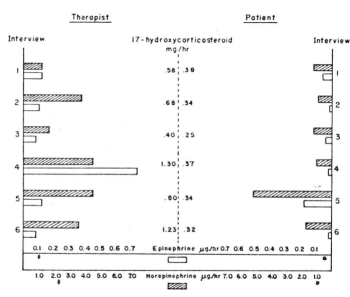

FIG. 7.—Data on therapist and patient during six psychotherapeutic interviews. Asterisk (*) indicates normal values for E and NE for patient. Double dagger (‡) represents normal values for therapist for same time of day when not engaged in psychotherapeutic process. Open bar indicates E excretion (micrograms per hour); hatched bar, NE excretion (micrograms per hour); 17-hydroxycorticosteroilds of same samples given in centre of figure as milligrams per hour.

to the therapy. This aspect is again shown with the sixth session where the therapist again shows high values in 17-hydroxycorticosteroid and an elevated NE excretion.'

We may summarize these findings of Elmadjian's group with patients by pointing out that aggressive emotional displays accompanying stresses are related to increased excretion of NE with or without increased excretion of

E. On the other hand, tense, anxious but passive emotional responses are accompanied by increased excretion of E in association with normal excretion of NE.

Individual Differences in Response in Relation to Performance of Stressful Tasks

I would like now to turn to some considerations of a different sort. These deal with individual differences in adrenal stress response in normal men. In 1943 Pincus and I (1943) reported a study of 17-ketosteroid excretion of army instructor pilots and civilian test pilots resulting from the stresses of flying airplanes and from operating a pursuit meter with airplane type controls. Timed urine samples were collected for several hours as controls before the flight or pursuit meter tests and again immediately after the test. The pursuit meter tests were conducted with different groups of men who operated the apparatus for either three or four hours. The urine samples were analyzed for 17-ketosteroids and usually increases in their output were found as a result of this relatively mild stress when the results of a number of runs for each individual were averaged. Since in a control study we found a diurnal rhythm for 17-ketosteroid excretion, corrections for this factor in relation to time of the test were made. Our published results showed that in general the higher a man's skill and the less his fatigue as measured by the decrement in his pursuit meter score, the less was his increase in 17-ketosteroid excretion following the test. It was as if the better performers needed to call less upon their adrenals to meet the situation. In this same study in a group of one-hour tests, air low in O_2 was breathed by the subjects during the pursuit meter operation. Performance was found to decline with the hypoxic conditions and 17-ketosteroid excretion was enhanced the greater the hypoxia. In a subsequent study, we reported lymphopenia accompanying the rise in 17-ketosteroids with the combined hypoxia and pursuit meter stress (Hoagland, Elmadjian and Pincus, 1946).

The studies took into consideration the diurnal rhythm of adrenal activity first demonstrated by work from our laboratory. This is an important consideration since the diurnal rhythm may entirely mask adrenal responses to weak stresses. Thus 17-ketosteroid output for men in their twenties during the first two hours after waking increases fifty per cent. on the average over sleep levels and tends to fall throughout the day. Other adrenal cortical indices show similar rhythms. If afternoon post-stress values of adrenocortical measures are compared with control values taken in the morning after rising, correction should be made for this rhythm. In general, for example, this amounts to an approximate average expectancy of twelve per cent. less 17-

7

ketosteroid output for 1–3 p.m. samples compared to morning control collections.

We have carried out further pursuit meter studies with and without hypoxia and determined changes in eosinophils and in urinary 17-ketosteroids, epinephrine, norepinephrine and electrolyte excretion resulting from the tests (Hoagland et al., 1955/6). In this series we were especially interested in individual differences as measured by scoring ability in relation to the adrenal responses.

The pursuit meter studies in this series were carried out in twenty normal men divided into four teams of five men each. Each man was tested from eight to ten times, once per week, in runs lasting either two or three hours. Incentive was maintained by an hourly pay rate plus a substantial cash bonus graduated in terms of each man's scoring ability.

These pursuit meter studies have been concerned not only with the adreno-cortical response as reflected in urinary 17-ketosteroids, Na, and K and eosinophil changes. We also measured effects of the stress on epinephrine and norepinephrine excretion. Total ketonic 17-ketosteroid determinations were made and urinary sodium and potassium were measured by flame photometry.

Team 1 underwent three-hour pursuit meter tests but without hypoxia and with five-minute rest intervals at the end of each hour. This team was the least stressed. Team 2 with two-hour runs without rest and breathing on an average thirteen per cent. O_2 was, as judged from their adrenal responses more stressed than team 1. Members of teams 3 and 4 breathed air containing only ten and a half per cent. O_2 for two-hour tests also without rest intervals. Subjectively the men of teams 3 and 4 reported that they were very much stressed and considerable after-effects were felt. One man of team 3 fainted in the course of one of the tests. Team 4 performed under conditions similar to those of team 3. Teams 3 and 4 averaged in age eighteen and seventeen years, respectively, while teams 1 and 2 were composed of older men with mean ages of thirty-two and twenty-six years, respectively.

Team 1 averaged forty-six per cent. of the time on target. Team 2 averaged forty per cent., team 3 averaged thirty-seven per cent., and team 4, twenty-seven per cent. While teams 3 and 4 operated under similar conditions team 3 was more highly motivated and more competitive. It was composed of high school students who were part-time employees at the laboratory and had more interest in the study. Team 4 was made up of high school boys who came in at weekly intervals for the test. These average team scores, we believe, reflect the increasing stress effects under which the teams operated. Team 1 showed an average drop of only eleven per cent. in eosinophils while team 2 showed a drop of twenty per cent. and team 3 a drop of forty-three per cent. Team 4 showed an average eosinopenia of thirty-eight per cent. The eosinophil drops thus also indicate the ascending order of stress for teams 1, 2 and 3. Teams 3 and 4 are not significantly different in terms of eosinopenia responses.

Epinephrine and norepinephrine values were not obtained for team 2. In the other teams most of the men had, in three out of their eight to ten runs, urinary epinephrine and norepinephrine measured in both control and test samples. The mean increases over controls of urinary epinephrine for team 1 were 109 per cent. following the stress and for team 3 epinephrine increased by 208 per cent. on the average over control levels. Norepinephrine values of teams 1 and 3, however, increased by fifty-four and thirty-two per cent. respectively over pretest values. The less highly motivated team 4 showed epinephrine and norepinephrine increases of 170 per cent. and 125 per cent., respectively. Since epinephrine increases represent increased activation of the adrenal medulla, these data further underscore the greater stress of teams 3 (208 per cent.) and 4 (170 per cent.) over team 1 (109 per cent.).

Increases in Na, K and 17-ketosteroids resulting from the stress were much greater for team 2 than for the lesser stressed team 1. But a curious discrepancy in these factors is seen in the cases of teams 3 and 4. Since the stresses of teams 3 and 4, who breathed an air mixture containing ten and a half per cent. O_2, by all the above criteria were considerably greater than those of teams 1 and 2 we might expect the stress increases of Na, K, and 17-ketosteroids for these teams also to be greater, but actually the Na increases of team 3 were less than those for team 2 and in the case of team 4 Na, on the average, was retained. Potassium excretion showed an actual decrease over control levels following stress for teams 3 and 4 and 17-ketosteroids showed no increases for teams 3 and 4. This is contrary to the results for teams 1 and 2 where stress 17-ketosteroids showed significant increases of eighteen per cent. and forty-eight per cent. respectively. These increases in stress 17-ketosteroids for teams 1 and 2 are in line with our previously reported findings in our pursuit meter studies for seventy normal men in this older age group.

There is, however, a marked age difference between the members of the first two teams and those of the third and fourth teams. The average age of team 1 is 32 years, that of team 2 is 26 years, but team 3 averages only 18 years of age and team 4 averages 17 years of age.

All of our previous stress studies have involved men over twenty. The failure of significant stress increase of 17-ketosteroids of the teams comprised of very young men, despite their big drops in eosinophils, is of special interest. It seems likely that the eosinophil decreases in teams 3 and 4 are mediated primarily by a large increased output of epinephrine rather than by adrenal corticoids in these younger groups. Clear evidence from our own and from other laboratories shows that persons who have experienced bilateral adrenalectomy show marked drops in eosinphils when injected with epinephrine.

Let us now compare the excretion of epinephrine and norepinephrine and 17-ketosteroid excretion in relation to eosinopenia. The data from team 1 indicate, in summary, enhanced excretion of epinephrine with the mild stress but relatively little eosinopenia or increase in 17-ketosteroid excretion. Teams 3 and 4 were more severely stressed as we have seen and our published data show the individual responses of these young men. The striking feature of the results is the relative absence of increase with stress of the rate of 17-ketosteroid excretion in these young men despite their eosinopenias. Though increases in NE were obtained in many of the experiments, the increases were not consistent and the results were quite variable. The eosinophil counts showed consistent decreases after the stress and the E excretion usually was increased. The decrease of the eosinophils was, on the average, thirty-five per cent. less than the control count, while the increased excretion of E averaged over one hundred per cent. One subject, however, showed no increase in E on all three occasions when he was subjected to the stress. It is of special interest that he is the identical twin brother of another member of this team. Adrenal cortical response measures were remarkably similar for these twin teammates, but the epinephrine and norepinephrine responses were very different.

In summary, under the conditions of these experiments, where subjects *under twenty years of age* underwent psychomotor stress under hypoxic conditions, the 17-ketosteroid excretion did not increase, the NE often did increase but not consistently. The eosinophils always decreased and E excretion usually increased following the stress. The stress eosinopenia appears to be correlated more often with E output than with 17-ketosteroid output. In six out of seventeen tests following stress, epinephrine excretion either did not change or it decreased with the fall of eosiniphils. In three of these cases 17-ketosteroid excretion also did not increase with stress. The most striking case is that of one subject who showed large drops in eosinophils following stress in his three tests in which E and NE were measured but showed no significant changes in E, and in two of the three tests he showed declines in NE following stress. In only one of these three tests did his 17-ketosteroids increase. These results suggest that there may be a factor other than epinephrine, norepinephrine or 17-hydroxycorticoids that may depress the eosinophils following stress. However, it should be borne in mind that adrenal steroids not metabolized to 17-ketosteroids and therefore not detected by our procedure may be involved in the eosinopenia, i.e. 17-desoxycorticoids such as corticosterone. Had we measured 17-hydroxycorticoids a clearer relation to the eosinopenia might have emerged.

Studies by Hill *et al.* (1956) of Harvard undergraduate rowing crews have shown rather small enhancements of 17-hydroxycorticoids and 17-ketosteroids with the stress of races. Their tests of cold exposure and one pursuit meter test also showed negligible adrenocortical activation either in terms of 17-hydroxycorticoids or of 17-ketosteroids. In view of our pursuit meter findings we feel that these differences may be influenced by age factors. Age data for the Harvard undergraduates was not given but presumably their average age was under twenty. Our comparisons of groups of men twenty to forty and forty-one to sixty years old in several stress

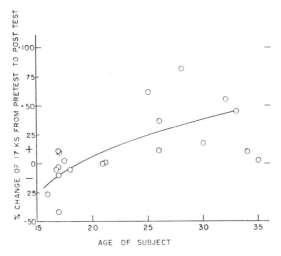

FIG. 8.—Relation of increase of ketosteroid output over control levels on stress to age of subject.

tests, including that of the pursuit meter, have shown no significant differences in mean per cent. 17-ketosteroid stress responses between these age groups (Hoagland *et al.*, 1953) but in the case of our teams 3 and 4 composed of boys sixteen to twenty years of age there is virtually no evidence of adrenal cortical response to our tests in terms of 17-ketosteroids or electrolyte responses. The seventeen-year-old subject on team 3 who fainted with hypoxia towards the end of one of his tests did not display enhanced 17-ketosteroid or electrolyte excretion on this occasion. His eosinophils dropped, however, by sixty per cent. and in the absence of evidence of adrenocortical stress we believe this effect was probably a result of enhanced epinephrine secretion. Unfortunately no epinephrine and norepinephrine determinations were made on this particular occasion.

Fig. 8 shows a plot of the stress output of 17-ketosteroids over control levels as a function of age for the men in this study. A line has been run through the scattered points to indicate the trend with age. It is clear that the older men tend to call more upon release of adrenocortical precursors of 17-ketosteroids. Unpublished data on the analyses of the urine samples for their individual 17-ketosteroid contents lend support to this hypothesis. Etiocholane-2α-11β-diol-17-one and etiocholane-3α-ol-11,17-dione excretion increased in the stress samples from team 1 but not from team 3. These substances are metabolites of hydrocortisone and cortisone. This is especially underscored by the fact that the older men were less stressed than the younger men by the conditions of the pursuit meter tests. Were this not the case we might expect the slope of the line to be steeper. Thus, team 1 operated without low O_2 content and thus with less stress than did the younger men of teams 3 and 4.

TABLE 18

INDIVIDUAL RANK ORDER OF SCORING ABILITY AND 17-KETOSTEROID EXCRETION

		1 Rank Order Lowest to Highest Final Mean Score		2 Rank Order Highest to Lowest Per Cent. Increase 17-ks		3 Corresponding Mean Values of Pre-test 17-ks, mg/hr.		4 Comparison Rank Orders, col. 1 to col. 2
Team 1								
(1)	.	S. K.	33	. S. K.	45	. 0·54	.	1–1
(2)	.	T. H.	38	. T. H.	18	. 0·45	.	2–2
(3)	.	F. U.	44	. F. U.	11	. 0·69	.	3–3
(4)	.	A. S.	56	. N. G.	11	. 0·68	.	4–5
(5)	.	N. G.	60	. A. S.	3	. 0·72	.	5–4

From Hoagland et al. (1955).

In our previous stress studies we reported that the most efficient performers on the pursuit meter were those showing the smaller stress increases in 17-ketosteroid output. We suggested that these more competent men needed to call less on the adrenal cortex to meet the task. In our study the seventeen- and eighteen-year-olds, while more stressed than the older men in terms of hypoxia and lack of rest intervals, show no evidence of adrenocortical stress responses. The data of team 1 are of interest in demonstrating the point that in comparing the individuals the better scorers show the smaller 17-keto-steroid responses to stress. In Table 18 the men of team 1 have been arranged from lowest to highest scorers and the per cent. increase in 17-ketosteroids with the stress is seen in general to follow an inverse relationship to score. In column 3, we give the pretest control levels of 17-ketosteroid outputs. One sees that in general the higher pretest values are correlated with lower per cent. stress increases. This indicates that pretest 'tension' may be accompanied by better scoring and also by a smaller per cent. rise in 17-ketosteroids from the already high pretest value. If the adrenal is working nearer its ceiling of activity before the test a lower per cent increase with stress is to be expected. Men 'keyed up' for the test may be expected to give higher control pretest values since they are already under psychological stress. Such men may also be expected to perform better than the indifferent subjects. The data of Table 6 are consistent with these interpretations.

The data of team 2 were not suitable for this type of analysis since the control samples were taken on days other than the stress days (but at the same time of day as the stress for purposes of correcting in this way for the diurnal rhythm). Thus no quantitative relationship existed between specific immediate pretest and post-test samples. Since teams 3 and 4 showed no adrenal cortical responses this analysis is also clearly not applicable.

A possible interpretation of the adrenocortical findings might be made as follows: suppose for example that the younger men excrete relatively large amounts of a 17-desoxy-C_{21} corticoid, such as corticosterone and/or aldosterone, rather than 17-hydroxycorticosteroids such as cortisol. Under these circumstances, Na would be better retained, as indeed it is. Corticosterone is not appreciably metabolized to 17-ketosteroid and their titer would not increase with stress. Nor, had we measured 17-hydroxycorticoids, would we have found much of an increase in these young men if they tend to secrete relatively more 17-desoxy-C_{21} corticoids and less 17-hydroxycorticoids. This situation might also apply to the Harvard crew studies. Do young men and those we have found to perform best on the pursuit meter respond to stress with low 17-ketosteroid outputs because corticosterone replaces cortisol and other 17-hydroxysteroids to some degree in their secretory products? This question is unanswered but warrants further study.

In summary of these results — comparison of adrenal reponse measures in normal men reflects the difficulty of the task as measured by scoring ability. Young men sixteen to twenty years of age appear to call very little on adrenal cortical mechanisms to meet stresses which enhance adrenocortical responses of older men. Eosinopenia correlates better with the urinary excretion of adrenaline than with that of 17-ketosteroids. Since eosinopenia may occur in some stress cases with no evidence of enhanced adrenocortical and adreno-medullary activity, it is suggested that a possible non-adrenal factor may be involved in the eosinopenia in addition to the effects of epinephrine and the 11-oxysteroids. We have also further evidence indicating that the better an individual's performance, the smaller is his per cent. increase in 17-ketosteroid output as a result of the stress. The data are at least consistent with the view that young men and efficient performers tend to secrete relatively more 17-desoxy-C_{21} steroids rather than 17-hydroxycorticoids.

I would now like to consider some recent studies from our laboratories of Elmadjian, Lamson, Hope and Pincus (in press) dealing with aldosterone excretion in anxiety states.

Urinary sodium retention accompanied with urine concentrations was noted by Elmadjian in a study of soldiers under combat stress in Korea (Pace *et al.*, 1956). In this same study when test injections of ACTH were were administered to infantrymen after a prolonged stress of five days of tough defensive action, no measurable increases in 17-hydroxycorticosteroid (17-OHCS) and 17-ketosteroid (17-KS) excretion was observed; however, there was a marked sodium retention. The pre-ACTH samples were also low in 17-OHCS and 17 KS values. The inference was drawn by Elmadjian *et al.* in these post-battle cases that though the adrenal cortex was non-responsive to ACTH with regard to 17-OHCS and 17-KS excretion, *the gland did secrete some hormone having potent sodium retaining activity*. Corticosterone and aldosterone were the two steroids considered as possible candidates, but neither of them nor their metabolites would be detected by methods used to measure 17-OHCS and 17-KS. More recently, Elmadjian *et al.* (unpublished) and also Venning and her associates in Montreal have independently observed that in certain anxiety states there is an increased excretion of the aldosterone. Thus Venning and Dyrenfurth (1956) found that anxiety induced by presenting scientific papers at meetings and the taking of examinations increased the excretion of aldosterone without increasing that of 17-OH corticoids. They found that 100 units of ACTH given to subjects produced a much smaller increase in output of aldosterone than did the taking of three-hour examinations. One subject showed a rise in rates from 2 to 20 μg. per twenty-four hours following the presentation of a paper at a meeting.

Elmadjian *et al.* have found a mean value of excretion of aldosterone of 4·1 μg./24 hrs (range 2·4 to 4·8) for a group of nine normal subjects. Fourteen schizophrenic subjects showed a wide range of values with a mean of 4·4 μg./24 hrs (range 1·2 to 10·0). It was noted that eight of the fourteen samples from the schizophrenics showed values of 2·4 μg./24 hrs. or less. The excretion rate was not related to the acuteness or chronicity of the schizophrenia as far as could be seen but rather to the emotional state of the subject when sampled, the more tense, anxious patients excreting the most aldosterone. A study of ten hospitalized patients diagnosed as suffering from anxiety neuroses showed marked elevations of aldosterone excretion. Six such patients excreted values of 10·0 to 12·5 μg./24 hrs. One, however, excreted a normal value of 2·4. A patient with anxiety neurosis and depression excreted 10 μg./24 hrs as did one with compensated malignant hypertension and anxiety state. Another hypertensive with anxiety yielded a value of 8·0, as did a patient diagnosed as having an anxiety neurosis and depression. A normal student after an oral doctoral examination excreted aldosterone at a rate of 10·0 μg./24 hrs.

Some of the high aldosterone excreters showed low excretion rates for 17-OHCS and normal amounts of 17-KS. It is of interest that Albeaux-Fernet and his associates (1957) reported that in chronic asthenia they obtained low 17-OHCS excretion with low 17-KS. They further observed that these subjects did not show increased 17-KS and 17-OHCS after ACTH injection. They presented data indicating increases in 17-desoxy C21 steroids. The inference drawn was that corticosterone was the major adrenal cortical steroid secreted in chronic asthenia. The similarity of these results and the inferences drawn to those of the Korean study earlier mentioned is worthy of note.

Elmadjian et al. have presented the following hypothesis relating to adrenal steroid biogenesis and metabolism as an attempt to relate the various findings in adrenal steroid excretion to stress, and especially explain, in part, the elevation of aldosterone in certain anxiety states. The adrenal cortex in the first stage of stress secretes 17-OHCS which are measurable by the Porter-Silber reaction and some 17-KS which may be estimated by the Zimmerman reaction. As the stress condition continues either the adrenal cortex ceases to show an increment of 17-OHCS with an increase in 17-KS, or the 17-OHCS secreted are more rapidly metabolized to 17-KS. As the stress is further sustained, both the excretion of 17-OHCS and 17-KS are low due primarily to inhibition of the 17-hydroxylating mechanism in corticosteroid biogenesis.

In summary, persons experiencing chronic or acute anxiety appear to show changes in the nature of the adrenocorticoid output with a suggested tendency to favour aldosterone and possibly corticosterone secretion rather than cortisol. Such an interpretation has also been made in relation to battle-stressed cases and it may be applicable in the stresses that have been described in studies of younger men operating the pursuit meter with anoxia. Much more work needs to be done before these points can be considered established but they are of considerable interest, particularly in relation to Selye's views about the possibility of a change in the nature of the adrenal output with stress.

DISCUSSION

In response to questions Dr Hoagland said that the bio-assay measured free adrenalin only and not esterified adrenalin. He emphasized that Elmadjian had shown, in a series of experiments, that exercise itself, unless it was extreme, had no effect on the output either of E or NE.

Dr Tanner asked what information existed as to a shift occurring under stress between the relative proportions of corticosterone and cortisol output. Dr Hoagland quoted experiments done in his laboratory on rabbits in which infusions of ACTH given every day for a matter of several weeks changed the pattern of secretion from high corticosterone/low cortisol, which is the normal rabbit pattern, to high cortisol/low corticosterone. The presumption was that a shift occurred in the activity of the enzyme system involved in hydroxylation at the number seventeen carbon atom (Kass, Hechter, Macchi and Mou, 1954).

Dr. Lacey said there were experiments which illustrated strikingly the importance of the significance of the stressor to the individual. One of these was by Dittes (1957) who studied GSR activity during a series of forty-four psychoanalytically orientated interviews with a neurotic patient. External observers rated the permissiveness, gentleness and understanding shown by the therapist at each interview and simultaneously the content of the interview. It was no surprise to find the patient showed more GSR activity when emotionally relevant material was being explored than when the topics were emotionally non-relevant, but the extent to which the GSR rate increased was found to depend upon the attitude of the therapist while this emotionally charged material was being discussed. When the therapist was at his most gentle and permissive and acceptant, and provided no cues of threat to the patient, then even quite highly charged topics failed to produce any increase in sympathetic activity; but on occasions when the therapist was not being permissive, then similar material produced a large response. Dittes had made the observation that the cues of threat derived from the therapist multiply with the cues provided by the discussion of emotionally charged material.

There had also been a study by Furer and Hardy (1950) on the adaptation of GSR in four very patient subjects who were exposed, day after day, to a graded series of intensities of pain by means of the Hardy-Wolff radiometer. This instrument produced a graded burn and experiments were continued until even the most intense burning pain produced hardly any change in GSR, this response having completely adapted. These people of course continued to perceive acutely the pain. When the social circumstances changed and the psycho-social stresses in the subject's life increased, the GSR response to the burn was likely to reappear. This happened, for example, to one subject who had to prepare a paper for a meeting later in the day. It happened also when one of the experimenters deliberately play-acted a hostility towards the subject; and in this instance both the play-acting experimenter and the subject produced a GSR response.

These two studies showed well the extent to which the individual created, so to speak, his own stressor; the response depending on circumstances and meaning, more than on the primary noxious agent.

CHAPTER 5

PREVENTION AND TREATMENT OF PSYCHIATRIC REACTIONS TO STRESS

PREVENTION AND TREATMENT OF PSYCHIATRIC REACTIONS TO STRESS BY PHYSIOLOGICAL AND PHARMACOLOGICAL MEANS

Dr W. Linford Rees

Department of Psychological Medicine, St Bartholomew's Hospital, London, and the Maudsley and Bethlem Royal Hospitals, London

In order to consider how responses to stresses may be modified by physiological and pharmacological means, it is necessary to devote our attention mainly to the processes, pathways and mechanisms involved in the organism's reactions to stressful stimuli. Consideration has to be given to the changes affecting the organism generally as well as to the relevant changes in the target organ.

The responses to stressful stimuli of all kinds, whether they are physical or psychosocial in origin, vary markedly between individuals. Also an individual may show marked variation in response to the same stress at different times.

In addition to genetic and constitutional factors accounting for these differences in reaction there are many other possible influences such as those described by Selye (1957) under the term conditional factors. These include level of salt and water intake, the effects of anti-inflammatory and other hormones etc. Reactivity will also be influenced by the type, degree and possible cumulative effects of stresses experienced in the immediate past. Furthermore, certain changes which occur in the organism relating to the state of the internal environment cause spontaneous alterations in the organism's reactivity to stressful stimuli of all kinds. Finally, it is possible to induce changes in the reactivity of the organism to stresses artificially, either by physiological means or by the action of pharmacological agents.

I will be dealing with these factors by reference to three fields of research in which I have personal experience.

The first field concerns a group of disorders in which the response to stress is readily observable, thus facilitating the study of correlations between the response and the manifold psychosocial situations and stimuli which are potentially stressful. The total group studied was 1,400 subjects consisting of 800 asthmatics, 100 patients suffering from nasal disorders (hay fever and vasomotor rhinitis), 100 patients suffering from urticaria or angioneuroti oedema and 400 normal subjects studied for control purposes.

The second field concerns recurrent periodic psychiatric and psychoso matic syndromes associated with the premenstrual phase. Particular referenc will be made to the relationship between attacks of these disorders and certain changes in the internal environment and their possible modification b physiological and endocrine means.

The third field relates to the effects of pharmacological agents in modifying responses to stress.

(1) *Asthma and Allied Disorders*

An investigation of the association between stressful or potentially stressfu stimuli and situations with the onset of asthma or with its precipitation during the course of the illness revealed that practically all the types of stimuli and situations described as stressful during our conference played a precipitating role in random samples of asthmatics of all ages and in both sexes. The types of neurotogenic situations described by Anthony, in his group o children, were all found to act as precipitants of attack in our asthmatic children. In particular, unsatisfactory parental attitudes were of paramoun importance in the production of emotional reactions in the child which, in fact, precipitated asthmatic attacks.

At the other extreme of the age range, different types of psychosocial situation were found to be stressful and associated with the precipitation of attacks. The most important were stresses associated with retirement and with grief reactions following bereavement, the role of which Lindemann (1950) has so lucidly described. Bereavement was also found to be one of many different types of stressful psychosocial situations associated with the onset or recurrence of attacks of vasomotor rhinitis and urticaria. There was no evidence of any specificity in the type of psychosocial stress at the onset or in precipitation of attacks during the illness.

The types of stressor capable of evoking the general adaptation syndrome with its characteristic physiological and biochemical changes listed by Selye (1950) were also found to be important in the precipitation of asthmatic attacks. Such stressors include allergic reactions, infections, excessive muscular exercise and marked emotional tension.

Multiple causation was found to be the rule in these psychosomatic disorders and any hypotheses regarding the responsible pathogenetic mechanisms should be able to account for the diversity of stimuli and processes which can precipitate attacks. Described physiologically, the changes occurring during an attack of asthma consist of swelling of the bronchial mucous membrane and/or contraction of the bronchoconstrictor muscle. Both urticaria and angioneurotic oedema involve locally increased vasodilatation and increased capillary permeability. It is possible to describe these in terms of biochemical changes involving acetyl choline, histamine and other possible chemical mediators, which can produce in the respective target organs all the relevant tissue changes which form the basis of the clinical manifestations.

An important consideration in this group of disorders is the principle of additive effects that different causal agents have on each other. It is well known that in many patients allergy alone is not sufficient to evoke an attack of asthma and that a state of emotional tension must also be present before the allergic reacton is manifested this way clinically. Clinical and experimental studies also show that infections can also exert summative effects with allergic and with emotional reactions.

The influence of the autonomic nervous system on tissue and organ functions provides a possible physiological explanation for at least some of these additive effects. Stimulation of the vagus can induce attacks of asthma, as can parasympatheticomimetic drugs such as pilocarpine and mecholyl. The production of asthmatic attacks in experimental animals by pilocarpine or mecholyl is greatly facilitated if the animal has a chemically induced bronchitis produced by chlorine. Acetyl choline also increases the effects of allergic reactions in some tissues.

There is evidence to suggest that the precipitation of attacks of asthma by allergic reactions, infections and emotional factors probably all involve chemical mediators such as histamine or acetyl choline which produce local tissue changes similar to those resulting from parasympathetic activity. This also has a direct bearing on the control of responses to stress by pharmacological means. It is possible to reduce or abolish the occurrence of attacks of these disorders to stressful stimuli by adrenergic drugs, by anti-cholinergic drugs and in vasomotor rhinitis and urticaria by antihistamines. These drugs act locally on the target organ and modify the local tissue reactions. It is also possible to demonstrate experimentally by the spirographic method of Herxheimer (1951) that a person's reaction to an inhaled allergen to which he is sensitive can be greatly diminished or prevented by hydrocortisone or adrenocorticotrophin.

The principles of multiple causation and summation of effects between factors have further important therapeutic implications and indicate the need for treatment to be directed towards as many of the causal factors as possible.

So far, we have mainly considered the efferent aspects of the autonomic nervous system but the afferent side is also important. For example in asthma, parasympathetic activity tends to produce increased, usually viscid, bronchial secretion, which tends to stimulate afferent impulses which, acting reflexly, further increase parasympathetic efferent activity. Thus a vicious circle is set up. This is probably one of the mechanisms underlying status asthmaticus.

(2) *Periodic and Recurrent Premenstrual Psychiatric and Psychosomatic Syndromes*

Turning now to the next field; in the above study some women suffering from asthma, vasomotor rhinitis and urticaria were found to have a distinct tendency to develop attacks at the premenstrual phase. Comparison of these patients with groups of asthmatic, vasomotor rhinitis and urticaria patients of similar age, marital status and parity, revealed the following two main differences:

(1) All patients with premenstrual occurrence of attacks exhibited in marked degree the manifold psychophysical manifestations of the premenstrual tension syndrome, whereas those without observable tendency for premenstrual attacks had no premenstrual tension or had it to a mild degree only.

(2) Plurality of causal factors, although a general rule in each disorder, was found to be evident to a much greater degree in the group with permenstrual attacks. This finding suggests that the pathogenetic mechanisms responsible for attacks are more readily evoked by a variety of stimuli in the group with premenstrual attacks than in the corresponding control groups.

As pointed out elsewhere (Rees 1953) the physiological and biochemical changes of the premenstrual tension syndrome closely correspond to the changes described by Selye (1950) occurring in the shock phase of the alarm reaction of the General Adaptation Syndrome.

I have carried out detailed longitudinal, endocrine and metabolic investigations extending over periods between four and nine months on a series of patients with premenstrual psychiatric syndromes. Among the patients studied were a group of patients who following recovery from a post partum psychosis (usually of the schizophrenic or depressive type) had a premenstrual recurrence of symptoms, qualitatively similar but quantitatively less marked than those of the initial psychosis.

In addition a number of patients with severe affective disorders occurring premenstrually were studied. Correlations were calculated between ratings of clinical state and metabolic and endocrine changes. Significant associations were found between attacks or exacerbations of illness an increased urinary excretion of acid-stable formaldehydogenic corticosteroids and a tendency for sodium and water retention with increase of body weight. Daily vaginal smears and endometrial biopsies revealed evidence of oestrogenic activity but not of progestogenic activity during the time of premenstrual occurrence of attacks. Selye (1950) finds that oestrogens are exceptionally strong stressor agents being one of the few which can evoke all the manifestations of the alarm reaction in adrenalectomized and hypophysectomized animals. The available evidence suggests that the changes in the internal environment of the body which are associated with premenstrual tension syndrome facilitate, in some patients, the manifestation of attacks of certain psychosomatic disorders and psychiatric syndromes, including affective disorders, schizophrenic reactions and neurotic symptoms.

We can attempt to modify the premenstrual syndromes by a number of different methods, the most simple being to deal with the hydration by restriction of salt intake and by giving of diuretics such as ammonium chloride or chlorethiazide. The finding of Selye (1957) that the action of inflammatory hormones on tissues is markedly influenced by the level of salt intake and the degree of hydration is of great interest in this connection. Experience shows that measures to reduce hydration alleviate some symptoms and manifestations but do not usually completely remove all symptoms of premenstrual syndromes. On the hypothesis that the manifestations of premenstrual tension syndrome are directly or indirectly, wholly or partially attributable to the actions of unantagonized oestrogens, the following methods have also been tried:

(1) Progestogens, either in the form of progesterone injection or by orally active ethisterone, norethisterone or dimethisterone. In a considerable proportion of patients so treated there were significant improvements above that obtained by dehydration measures alone. A proportion of patients, however, did not respond to any of these therapies and further research is required to ascertain the reason for this and to discover more effective therapeutic agents.

(3) Modification of Stress Responses by Pharmacological Means

Just as there is considerable variation between individuals in responses to stresses, there are marked variations between individuals in response to pharmacological agents. This is one of the great areas of ignorance in the field of psychopharmacology. We do not yet know why some patients respond satisfactorily to a particular drug whereas patients who are clinically similar may not derive any benefit. Furthermore, individuals may vary in response to the same drug at different times. It would seem probable that these variations are caused by intrinsic as well as environmental factors. That environmental factors can be important is shown in animal experiments which demonstrate that the toxic effects of benzedrine are much greater when the animals are in a group than when alone. The effects resulting from activation between animals in a group reduced considerably convulsive

8

threshold to benzedrine. Experience I have had in carrying out double blind clinical trials with tranquillizing and anti-depressant drugs in a ward for disturbed patients at the Bethlem Royal Hospital strongly suggests that the behaviour of patients is exponentially related to the size and structure of the group.

Recent research has shown that individual differences in response to drugs may also be determined by genetic factors. At the animal psychology department of the Maudsley and Bethlem Hospitals selective breeding has successfully produced two distinct strains of rats referred to as the Maudsley emotionally reactive and emotionally non-reactive strains. The method used for assessing emotionality was the measurement of responses of rats to the mildly stressful situation known as the Hall Open Field Test in which the animal is exposed to a strange arena and to sound and light stimulation of moderate intensity. The animal's responses on successive days were observed, particularly the defaecation response which is generally regarded as a specially sensitive indicator of fear. On the basis of scores derived from these observations, selective breeding for high and low defaecation was carried out.

The development of conditioned fear responses in the two strains has been studied by Singh (personal communication) who found, as predicted, that the emotionally reactive strain acquired conditioned fear responses more readily than the non-reactive strain. Singh has also studied the effects of stimulant and depressant drugs on the acquisition and extinction of conditioned emotional responses. He found that stimulant drugs were effective for strengthening the emotional response, but only in the reactive strain whereas the depressant drug such as Chlorpromazine had a much greater effect on the responses of the non-reactive strains. These findings suggest that the effects of a drug are determined, in part at least, by the behavioural characteristics of the animal as measured by the Hall Open Field Test of emotionality.

Time does not permit full discussion of all the relevant aspects of the new psychotrophic drugs. In brief, the results of studies of psychotrophic drugs on unlearned behaviour, on learned reactivity such as conflict induced behaviour, stress induced behaviour and avoidance responses indicate that the tranquilizing drugs fall into two distinct classes:

Group I consists of

(a) Phenothiazine derivatives e.g. Chlorpromazine and many others more recently introduced.

(b) Reserpine and other alkaloids derived from *Rauwolfia serpentina*.

(c) Diphenyl methane derivatives such as Benactyzine, Atarax, etc.

Group II includes central relaxants such as Meprobamate and Mephenesin

The two groups showed marked differences in action. The drugs in Group I have marked effects on the autonomic nervous system both centrally and peripherally. They are also able to antagonize the actions of acetyl choline, histamine and sertonin in isolated intestine. They also differ from Group II in their effects on the electroencephalogram and regarding taming effects and effects on avoidance reactions.

Experimental evidence indicates that both reserpine and chlorpromazine have important influences on the hypothalamus. Both have a taming effect on aggressive behaviour in monkeys, and both abolish the orienting response in the dog. However, reserpine and chlorpromazine differ in some of their central effects, e.g. reserpine reduces the threshold and prolongs the duration of seizure activity in the limbic system, whereas chlorpromazine has little or no such effect. Chlorpromazine has a greater effect on the electrocortico-gram than reserpine, this effect being apparently mediated through its sup-posed major site of action, namely the reticular activating system. Mepro-bamate and mephenesin on the other hand have no peripheral effects on the autonomic nervous system and slight or no effects on the transmission of impulses through the central autonomic mechanisms.

Research into the biochemical, physiological, electrophysiological, endo-crine and clinical effects of psychotrophic drugs is a promising and fruitful field which should provide further valuable information on the precise changes involved in reactions to stresses and the processes and mediating pathways so involved and also the means by which they may be effectively modified and may even eventually provide solutions to the many outstand-ing problems in this complex field (Rees, 1956, 1958).

DISCUSSION

Professor Gerard questioned whether most of the present psycho-active drugs exerted their effects by altering peripheral mechanisms. One could often counter-act the peripheral actions without influencing the total behavioural effects.

One of his colleagues had been studying the action of these drugs on the lobster cardiac ganglion because this was a simple collection of nine neurones which it seemed might serve for an analysis of the mechanism of action. So many com-binations could exist however, even between nine neurones, that the system was too complicated to understand thoroughly. When simple physiological para-meters such as excitability, action potentials and so on were measured, however, it emerged that every single drug tested acted in a somewhat different manner. He said he thought it unlikely that any of these drugs acted on any one particular part of the central or peripheral nervous systems.

PREVENTION AND TREATMENT OF PSYCHIATRIC REACTIONS TO STRESS BY PSYCHO-SOCIAL MEANS

J. D. SUTHERLAND

Tavistock Clinic, London

When we look at the psychiatric and social-psychiatric measures taken in our current therapeutic and preventive endeavours, the first point we may note is their extraordinary variety. A wide range of actions, from apparently minor to much more comprehensive alterations, either in the social environment or in the intra-psychic systems of the individual, or in both, or at times in some of the body substrates by physical measures, can alter or redistribute psychological forces so that a less stressful state obtains. Often the previous equilibrium, held by relationships with people in the outer world or with fantasy figures in the inner world, seems to be regained spontaneously after an upset. Sometimes, despite intensive psychiatric action, the disturbed state may persist or even deteriorate.

A second prominent feature of present treatment and prevention is the almost complete lack of accurate criteria by which we can describe in specific terms either the aims of our measures or their results.

This confusing scene is not surprising when we bear in mind the number and complexity of the inter-related open systems contributing to behaviour and the consequent difficulties in identifying the variables which may be playing the critical roles in determining the end-states. If, however, we assume the central role at the psychosocial level of the experience of anxiety in psychological stress and the enormous range of stimuli which can arouse it, two broad questions emerge:

(a) What account can we give of personality and its development? On the one hand the mentally healthy person acquires a considerable capacity to use most anxiety experiences constructively, that is, he masters proneness to anxiety by the time he reaches adulthood. On the other hand many individuals remain liable to the arousal of undue anxiety, i.e., anxiety which is not related to external danger but to some internal threat and are left at the mercy of inadequate and stereotyped ways of dealing with it.

(b) Leaving aside deprivations in the material environment, can we identify features in the social environment which have a general tendency to arouse anxiety, and if so, what measures can we take to remove these agents or to lessen their effects?

Our answers to these questions will clearly provide the bases for both our therapeutic and our preventive actions. In what follows, I shall outline an approach to these questions based on my experience in the Tavistock Clinic, a unit in a national health service confronted with the out-patient psychological illnesses. I shall also draw on what I have learned from my colleagues both in the Clinic and in the Tavistock Institute of Human Relations.

Starting with the adult, we can regard his personality as made up of a large number of dynamic psychic structures, each of which is an open system in transaction to varying degrees with the social environment and with other inner psychic systems. By the term 'transaction', I mean an on-going relationship in which there is a reciprocal interaction. Each person is involved in the relationship in an active way with his or her needs constantly affecting the behaviour of the other. These systems vary greatly in their mode of activity and in their topological position within the personality as a whole.

From the point of view of the psychiatric observer the psychic systems within the individual can be put into two main groups:

(a) those supplying the inner impetus to action, i.e. those determining what we commonly term 'drives' or 'needs', and which I shall describe as the *personal-relationship need systems* to draw attention to certain essential features of their activities;

(b) those concerned with the *control and regulation* of the previous systems and with the development of increased power in exploring and manipulating the environment in the interests of the need systems.

The *personal-relationship need systems* seem to stem originally from species-specific behaviour patterns which evolve within the infant. Early experience rapidly leads to a splitting off of systems derived from experiences associated with pain or trauma. Eventually the need systems can therefore be grouped into two divisions: those for which we use the word 'egosyntonic', i.e. which belong to a central organizing structure; and those which are split off or repressed from this central system. (I shall use the words 'split off' or 'repressed interchangeably in this context.)

The *controlling systems* can also be separated into two main groups. There is assimilated by the central system much of the experience with significant people in the early environment, and hence much of the cultural pattern in which the individual is reared. This central adaptive control we commonly speak of as the ego. There is also a more primitive type of control system derived from the earliest processes of inhibition of the personal need systems. These primitive systems in contrast with the controls exercised by the ego are characterized by their relative fixity and stereotypy. (These primitive controls are covered by the psycho-analytic term, the super-ego.)

The word 'system' indicates that these structures are organized and seek to effect certain kinds of activity. The particular goals sought by the need systems are derived from the totality of previous experiences. Thus a personal-relationship need system is a highly-patterned structure which includes within it images of the objects sought with associated expectations from people or their substitutes. The central ego is characterized by the particular methods adopted by the individual in his attempts at mastery and control over the need systems.

All of the psychic systems are inter-related functionally, and in the adult their relative strengths and capacities can only be conceived as stemming from a continuous process of inter-related development. Also, the boundaries of these systems are fluid and difficult to define.

It is important to keep in mind that all need systems, whether repressed or not, are continually seeking relations with people in the social environment, though the pressure they exert may fluctuate. In particular, the individual seeks to fit people into the patterns of the repressed systems, and at times even to create situations that force others into them. Thus, the system underlying 'chip-on-the-shoulder' behaviour will seek out, or will lead the individual to provoke, in the behaviour of others justifications for it to go into action. That is to say, the repressed need systems, because they have been split off early in life under the influence of traumatic pain or anxiety, tend to retain the quality described by the word 'fixation'; they are apparently not susceptible to the modification by learning which takes place in the egosyntonic systems through the constant transactions with people.

In a healthy person, the main need systems are egosyntonic and of such a character that a manifold set of relationships with his society is sought and maintained, thereby providing satisfaction to the higher order systems of development. Understanding, trust and toleration in personal relations increase with the consequent growth of constructive relationships embracing a wider range of people and social purposes. The central regulating systems in such a person are being enriched throughout life and this constant enrichment provides a motivational growth and support. The relatively free transactions between the systems themselves (greater communication) in the healthy person also means that he responds more as a whole, is more integrated in assessing inner and outer reality.

Mental ill-health by contrast arises from a breakdown in the amount and scope of the transactions that the individual is able to make with his social environment. The individual here, for instance, has too much generalized inhibition because of over-active primitive controls, again, the dominant personal-relationship need systems, even if egosyntonic, may be so incompatible with, or inappropriate to, the society in which he lives that the social environment denies him the necessary interchanges.

In considering therapeutic and preventive measures, the following four areas can be separated, although there is a good deal of overlap amongst them.

A. Therapeutic measures designed to alter the intra-psychic systems of the individual personality to increase his freedom and adaptive powers.

B. Therapeutic measures which combine the previous aim along with the simultaneous alteration of another individual or others who are involved in on-going transactional relationships with the individual.

C. Preventive measures to facilitate the optimal growth and development of the person.

D. Those preventive measures concerned with removing or minimizing the effects on adults of stressor situations in the social environment.

A. Therapeutic Measures to Alter the Intra-psychic Systems of the Individual, i.e. Individual Psychotherapy

It is useful to restrict the term psychotherapy to those procedures which attempt to let the patient become conscious of some of his hitherto unrecognized personal-relationship needs within a relationship with the therapist. The aim here is to bring these need systems within the boundaries of the ego. By recognizing them the individual can achieve a greater measure of control either by effecting a reduction in their pressure or by the development of better adaptation.

In psychotherapy the intensive analytical methods and the psychotherapies which are derivatives from them can be distinguished.

I. PSYCHOANALYSIS

The classical psychoanalytic method is the most comprehensive and systematic of these methods because it creates a relationship in which it is possible for the patient progressively to fit the analyst in turn into virtually all the roles in his repressed need systems and, in particular, the earliest ones. Psychoanalytical theories are psychosocial theories, the meaning of symptoms or behavioural difficulties was discovered by Freud when he took the step of interpreting some of the *relationships* that the patient was seeking to make with him as due to the transference to the analyst of infantile needs. Put in another way we can say that the psychic systems, as Talcott Parsons remarks of all open systems, are only to be studied at their boundaries, that is in their processes of transaction. Repressed systems only become more open when the transference relationship is allowed free scope and when the therapist can make clear to the patient the roles into which the latter is trying to put him.

What can be achieved with our present knowledge and skill in effecting intra-psychic change is all too often uncertain. With enough treatment, the pressure of some of the need systems can be altered to the point of their virtual disappearance. With less therapeutic effort, as is the rule, the diminution in some permits a redistribution of the psychic economy so that more acceptable and more satisfying relationships for the self as a whole can be attempted and developed into an enduring pattern.

Practical considerations preclude psychoanalysis from ever being a treatment which can be offered on a wide scale. The continued practice and study of the classical psychoanalytic method, however, is needed because of its value as a research instrument. It is now essential that more rigorous scientific work is carried out by psychoanalysts both on methods and in relating hypotheses to other observations, especially those of early development. Regarding the study of the psychoanalytic method, it is particularly important that this work should be possible within the hospitals and clinics where all the necessary observations can be made and the requisite tests developed for more accurate diagnosis and assessment of change. Much of the lack of rigorous scientific work into the process of psychoanalysis is due to the fact that full-scale analysis is almost entirely carried out with private patients in a setting which cannot offer the facilities necessary for the testing of more precisely formulated hypotheses.

2. APPLIED ANALYTICAL METHODS

(a) *Analytically Based Psychotherapy for the Individual.* The practical limitations of the classical psychoanalytic method have led to many attempts to find short cuts. These less intensive methods are usually based on psychoanalytic concepts and try to achieve their aims of increasing insight and integration by identifying the most prominent difficulties and then concentrating on the need systems underlying these. Useful results have been achieved but the criteria for choice of case and the assessment of results still rests largely on clinical judgments with the limitations these impose.

(b) *Group Psychotherapy.* Group therapy is mentioned here as in individual method' because the therapist's work is concerned primarily with the alteration of each individual patient's psyche so that he can make better relationships in his own external world.

As with individual methods, here too there has been a wide range in the approaches used and results in relation to initial assessment are similar to those obtained with individual methods.

All the lessons of psychotherapy point to certain requirements as essential if alteration of the conflicting need systems is to be achieved. The therapist should be available at times of crisis when the repressed systems are most open. He must be able to provide continuity of treatment and there must be, of course, adequate skill and understanding in the conduct of the treatment. If to these requirements is added the great incidence of the psychological illnesses it cannot but be concluded that our present psychiatric institutions are unable to meet the needs of the situation. Most of them are forced to operate in terms that play into the repressive solutions of the individual. In conformity with the more modern psycho-biological viewpoint, many hospitals are striving, however, to become more open systems with much greater communication with the community and with more explicit handling of the patient's difficulties as psychosocial problems.

With the increased recognition of the nature of the psychological disorders, there is a fairly widespread effort to create in the community a network of people who will be able to provide the requirements of the therapeutic figure, viz. that he will be available, be constant and have enough skill and understanding to tolerate the acting out within the therapeutic relationship of some of the repressed needs of the disturbed person.

During the last ten years my colleagues and I have been training various professional groups all of whom are faced with psychotherapeutic tasks, e.g. general practitioners, public health officers, family case-workers and probation officers. The training has consisted of having groups meet weekly over a long period to discuss the treatment of their own cases. By devoting about fifteen per cent. of our senior staff time (including psychiatrists, psychologists and social workers) we have recently been seeing in weekly sessions approximately 200 professional workers — 20-30 psychiatrists, 80-100 general practitioners and medical specialists, 20-30 public health doctors and health visitors, 30-40 family case-workers, and 40-50 probation officers. In addition to conducting these training groups, there is also a permanent 'open system' whereby those who have been through the training period can continue to get help with their more difficult cases.

Turning to research, the great need is for accurate assessment methods of the personality. These would improve diagnosis and would lead to greater precision in our conceptual formulations; they would also enable us to measure the changes effected by treatment. Research is also needed into the nature of the therapeutic process itself.

A first requirement for improved diagnosis and the measurement of change would appear to be methods which will indicate as objectively as possible the nature and relative strengths of the repressed needs and the controlling systems and thereby give some measure of the capacity of the central ego to tolerate their re-emergence in consciousness. The most striking feature in this whole field has been the extraordinary difficulty in evolving such measures. Possibly the appropriate observation point has not been right for getting at the properties and inter-relations of the various need systems. In the Tavistock Clinic we have been following two lines. One is a *self-assessment inventory* which is used to ascertain the constellations amongst psychological symptoms and character traits. (The second line of work is described in the next section.) Many assumptions exist about these groups under the various diagnostic labels, but few have actually been put to the test. By taking a large number of the common statements of patients about symptoms and character traits (about 900 in all) Sandler (Sandler, 1954; Sandler and Pollock, 1954A & B; Kanter and Sandler, 1955) has shown that some of these assumptions are supported but others are not.

In the light of his findings, for instance, it emerges that functional dyspepsia is not an isolated physical symptom but occurs as a rule with other physical and psychological indications of anxiety. The term 'nervous indigestion' therefore seems an appropriate one. A further provisional study did not confirm the widely held view that functional dyspepsia and actual gastric ulcer are to be found in different personality types. The involvement of the stomach in this group of people is therefore shown to be part of a potentially varied response. In contrast, anal defaecatory symptoms show no correlation with other bodily manifestations but do so with the character traits Freud associated with the anal phase.

B. *Treatment of Individuals in Close Transactional Relationships*

Certain social relationships, e.g. the marital relationship, the parent-child and sibling relationships, obviously play a much more prominent part than others in the lives of all of us. As we should expect, there tend to be in these relationships strong and persistent attempts from the repressed need systems of both parties to seek realization, so that there is ample scope for serious disturbance. Conversely, these relationships have also a high potential for change because they are active on-going transactions stemming from basic needs. If one source of tension can be lessened, the whole quality of the relationship and the satisfaction it gives to both parties can often be improved. In recent years my colleagues and I have had a good deal of experience in treating marriages in trouble. Often one or both partners present a psychopathology that would constitute a formidable therapeutic task if dealt with as an individual problem. By taking the relationship as the primary object of treatment, the way in which parts of each person use the other for aims inimical to the main desires of both can be exposed. The support that each can then give the other leads to a much more constructive relationship with a diminution of tension that has beneficial effects spreading to children and to work relationships.

Experience with close relationships has also stimulated new ways of approaching the psychodiagnostic problem because the various need systems determining relationships are seen clearly within these close relationships. With marital partners each is asked to go through a check list and describe the following 'people': self, partner, mother, father, ideal self, ideal partner, self as he thinks he is seen by his partner. From one marriage fourteen people are described, and the ways in which these 'people' fit can be studied. Thus, in one marriage, the wife's ideal partner resembled closely the picture of her father, whereas her husband was described as markedly different. The relatively objective pictures of the contradictions that arise between these ideals and the actual relationship achieved that can be given by tests of this kind will, we hope, be useful in assessing the source of difficulties in the marriage and in providing a measure for change after treatment. (See Dicks, 1953.)

Relationship work with the family has considerable similarity in principle to that with the marital relationship with the addition here of therapeutic work on one or more of the children in the family. This pattern of work is a common one with most child guidance clinics, and, as already mentioned, now it is also becoming more widespread through the increased skills of other professional groups who have to deal with the family, e.g. social workers, probation officers and health visitors.

C. Preventive Action to Facilitate the Optimal Growth and Development of the Person

It is generally assumed that the most radical preventive measures for reducing the incidence of mental illness will lie in the creation of a body of knowledge from which the requisites for healthy personality development can be stated. Such a body of knowledge would not only enable us to help bring up our children more successfully, but would also lead to earlier diagnosis of difficulties. While the role of the feeding transaction plays a dominant part in the life of the infant and its influence is not to be under-estimated, it is being more and more recognized that other forces may be operative. My colleague John Bowlby (1958) has recently stated 'the nature of the child's tie to its mother may well be mediated by a number of instinctual response systems which are partially independent of one another and which wax and wane in activity at different periods of the infant and young child's life; and that for instance the responses of clinging and following, which seem to reach their zenith in the second and third years, require far more attention than they have yet been given.'

We are here faced with the need for a vastly increased volume of research to establish validated principles and especially for studies in which the insights into possible early developmental processes obtained from psycho-analytic studies can be correlated with direct observations of early behaviour.

In keeping with the growth of our more comprehensive biological and psychosocial understanding, even in child development we have to guard against over-isolation of phenomena. The bearing and rearing of children create critical phases in the reproductive cycle of the family and as such they are heavily influenced by cultural and social pressures on the family. Preventive measures here can only come from the combined work of many disciplines. After the early years, the contributions to the development of the personality, especially to the ego, from experiences in the family, in school and at work, are possibly greater than would be indicated by the amount of theoretical interest at present taken in these later stages. The recent work of Funkenstein, King and Drolettes (1957) on the mastery of stress is suggestive in this connection. These writers found, for instance, that while the initial reaction to stress characteristic of each individual can be shown to be related to biological factors and early experiences, the capacity to master stress is not correlated with the initial pattern but with different personality variables. That is to say the central ego systems may acquire 'strength' independently by later experience.

D. Preventive Action in the Social Environment of Adults

(a) STRESS IN WORKING GROUPS

Relationships in working groups constitute a large part of the social experience of most adolescents and adults. Tensions within groups, and between the various working groups in larger organizations, are a potent source of stress on their members and great progress in understanding the nature and origins of these stresses is now being made.

There would be general agreement that 'the effective performance of a primary task (i.e. the task which a group is created to perform) can provide an important source of satisfaction for those engaged upon it.' (Rice, 1958.)

From the study of working groups involved in the Longwall Method of Coal-getting, Trist and Bamforth (1951) have described the socio-technical system constituted by the modern industrial primary group. By this term they seek to convey the complex inter-relations of occupational roles and social relationships that have to be matched to the technical resources by which the primary task of the group is performed, and especially to any technical innovations, if the working conditions are to be satisfactory both for the productivity and well-being of the worker.

Trist has demonstrated the diminution in psychological disturbances which occurs through change in the work organization of groups. Reference may also be made to Rice's (1958) recent book *The Ahmedebad Experiment* where he describes the remarkable increases in productivity following changes based on similar principles.

The diagnosis of the sources of stress in socio-technical systems may remain for some time yet predominantly the role of the highly trained social scientist, but the implementation of remedies will only be successful with increased understanding and skill on the part of managers and executives. It must also be emphasized that in this area the social scientist may well come up against forces inherent in the values of our society as a whole.

Last autumn the Tavistock Institute of Human Relations planned in conjunction with Leicester University a pilot training conference in Group Relations (Trist and Sofer, 1959). The aim of the conference was to increase among those already in responsible positions understanding of human interaction, i.e. they should learn to perceive social processes more clearly so that they could act more effectively. This was done by providing not only intellectual instruction but *experience* in groups with opportunities for participants to deepen their understanding of the feelings which animate groups and increase their sensitivity concerning the effects of these feelings on behaviour. At a follow-up meeting six months after the conference, the subsequent experiences of those who had attended indicated that considerable progress could be made in achieving the original aims.

(b) INTRA- AND INTER-GROUP TENSIONS IN THE HOSPITAL

The study of intra-group tensions and of the tensions aroused by the relations between groups in institutions with a view to restructuring the patterns of relationship so that these tensions can be minimized is one which is arousing much interest amongst psychiatrists. The well-known work of Stanton and Schwartz (1954) showed all too clearly how inadequate inter-group relations, and especially inadequate communication arrangements, can militate against the therapeutic work of the doctors and nurses in the mental hospital. The number of mental hospitals attempting to improve their internal conditions is increasing, but unless there is adequate under-standing and emotional acceptance of the consequences of such efforts amongst the senior staff of the hospital, the change process is not likely to proceed far. Thorough appreciation of the issues must also lead to the external relations of the hospital with its surrounding community becoming the object of study. It is to be hoped that the nature and the implications of change processes in hospitals as in other social organizations will be appre-ciated lest premature enthusiasm and over-simplification lead to disappoint-ment.

That a full analysis of the nature of a social institution in relation to its therapeutic task with the subsequent creation of a structure appropriate to this task can be very effective was strikingly shown by the results Trist obtained from the Civil Resettlement Units created at the end of the war to help returned prisoners of war (Curle and Trist, 1947–8). Careful follow-up established the more successful re-adaptation to civil life of those who had gone through these units compared with those who did not.

SUMMARY

The appreciation of the inter-relatedness of all personality processes from the biological through the psychological to the social is not new. It is, how-ever, beginning to be more meaningful and influential on our actions and it may well be that we shall have to look afresh at the whole nature of our therapeutic institutions in the psychosocial field at any rate. Four areas of work were separated because they seemed to provide convenient headings for review and discussion and also because they contain, I hope, our funda-mental problems. These were:

(i) Therapeutic action concerned with the intra-psychic systems of the individual.

(ii) Therapeutic action concerned with close transactional relationships; for example in the family setting.

(iii) Preventive action related to growth and development.

(iv) Preventive action related to improving the adult social environment.

Actions in these fields are all inter-related. Our psychiatric clinics do not yet reflect this connectedness but there are signs that they are trying to do so. One great change that has begun is the alteration in the position and bound-aries of the hospitals and clinics. These systems are not only being moved into more intimate connections with their social space; their boundaries are also beginning to become highly permeable. The resultant increased relatedness to the social environment as a whole should create a practical field appropriate to research and to the development of more unified theory and hence to more adequate treatment and prevention.

DISCUSSION

Mr Trist described the improvement both in output and absenteeism following change of the method of working in a coal mine. This was an example of how the response of the human to stress is affected by a specifically social factor, the form of group organization or social structure.

Some patterns of work organization were better than others in enabling the individual to meet environmental stress adaptively. Especially since the early years of the last war, a body of knowledge had been coming into existence which enabled us better to understand what group patterns of work were stress absorbing and what patterns were not. We were becoming able to choose more surely between alternative forms of social organization so that at one and the same time the psychological health of the individual could be benefited and the standard of his performance improved.

Mr Trist illustrated this by studies carried out in the mining industry (Trist and Murray, 1958). Work at the coal face was by common consent among the most stressful of industrial occupations and Halliday (1949) in Scotland, showed that the incidence in stress illness among miners working at the coal face was about two and a half times that found among any other occupational group in Scotland. A colliery medical officer, the late Dr D. E. Dickson (1936) had suggested that this was not simply to be attributed to industrial conflict and economic depression, but rather that it might be related to the change-over from one method of mining to another, that is, from traditional board and pillar working to longwall conveyor mining.

In traditional board and pillar working, living examples of which were still to be found in the older coal fields, the total work cycle that comprised the coal-getting task was carried out by one small group of people usually no more than six in number. These were one social group with one pay slip. The group was self-selected and each member regarded the others as mates. Members of the group all carried out the entire range of tasks, sharing the more inconvenient with the more convenient shifts. This was the traditional group which had a quality which could be designated as *responsible autonomy* (Trist and Bamforth 1951).

Such a group was highly adaptive to the changing and unpredictable character of the underground situation and indeed had been evolved through generations of experience in this particular type of dangerous environment. It was, in fact, a highly sophisticated social structure. In it the miner had to work hard, but however much he was discontented with managers and owners he was not psychologically stressed as he became when conventional longwall work was introduced.

Under this system there was a much larger total cycle group with forty-one men in the faces Mr Trist had studied and more than twice that many in some longer faces. The forty-one men had been split into fourteen different task groups with different goals and different pay notes. There were five such task groups on the first shift, three on the second and six on the third. Thus the traditional unitary coal face group had been atomized into a large number of segregated single task groups according to the prevailing fashion in production engineering which seeks to break work down into the smallest possible units. But because the overall cycle group was now only an aggregate it had no mechanism for internal self-regulation and regulation had to be supplied entirely from the outside by management. In the underground situation this was possible only to a limited extent so that the small component groups competed, conflicted or colluded one with the other to various degrees, with the result that the work-cycle progress tended to become impaired.

As a remedy for this situation an overall organization had been created which welded these single task groups into a unified social whole concerned with cycle completion as a group goal, while maintaining the longwall method of work, (Wilson and Trist, 1953). Such a group organization was already emerging spontaneously in certain pits (Higgin, 1960). In this overall organization members shared a common pay note, exchanged tasks and shifts according to principles they had evolved for themselves and the relationship of 'mate' extended to all members of the cycle group.

In Tables 19–21, the results were given from two coal faces, one organized on conventional lines with forty-one men in fourteen different groups; another using exactly the same technology and equipment, the same seam of coal, but organized on the new principle called *composite*.

In Table 19 it could be seen how the conventional organization restricted a man to one task with one little work group. In the composite work method each man varied his work task, varied his shift and varied the task groups with which he worked.

We could take withdrawal from the work situation as a measure of socio-logical casualty (Hill and Trist, 1953, 1955). The environments of the two faces were about as similar as they could be, but the difference in absenteeism indicated in Table 20 was striking. A method was devized by which a quite accurate estimate of potential productivity of a particular coal face could be estimated. In Table 21 the performance of the task of coal-getting in the two systems was compared with reference to this potential productivity. It was clear that the system that was less stressful in the psychological sense was also much the more productive.

Interviews and group discussions with the men in three different coal fields had shown that the men themselves also much preferred the composite system which had indeed emerged from them as much as from the management. It was

TABLE 19

VARIETY OF WORK EXPERIENCE
(Averages for whole team)

Aspect of Work Experience	Conventional Longwall	Composite Longwall
Main Tasks worked at . .	1·0	3·6
Different *Shifts* worked on . .	2·0	2·9
Groups worked with . . .	1·0	5·5

TABLE 20

ABSENCE RATES
(Per cent. of possible shifts)

Reason for Absence	Conventional Longwall	Composite Longwall
No reason given . . .	4·3	0·4
Sickness and other . . .	8·9	4·6
Accident	6·8	3·2
Total .	20·0	8·2

TABLE 21

PRODUCTIVITY AS PER CENT. OF ESTIMATED FACE POTENTIAL

Conventional Longwall	Composite Longwall
78·0	95·0

strongly backed by the local unions and the older miners who had experience of working the old board and pillar system recognized the composite longwall system as the natural inheritor of the old tradition.

What was of particular importance to the social psychologist was that such a large primary work group should be capable of such a high degree of self-regulation. It was this responsible autonomy which seemed to overcome the worker's 'alienation' and thus reduce his stress, even under difficult conditions. It had not been so far commonly accepted that such responsible autonomy could be created in such relatively large groups.

9

CHAPTER 6

GENERAL DISCUSSION

GENERAL DISCUSSION (A)

Denis Hill

Institute of Psychiatry, University of London

When I was a medical student the word 'stress' was rarely heard. Certainly when I started my psychiatric training it was not a concept that was much used, and to check this I looked up the text books upon which we depended at that time. There is no reference to it in the earlier editions of Henderson and Gillespie nor indeed, had Slater, Mayer-Gross and Roth very much to say about it in their recent text. Nor can we find the word used in either the earlier or later writings of the psychoanalysts. Freud did not use the term, nor did Fenichel. The concept was quite foreign to the psychologists of thirty years ago. McDougall makes no reference to it, nor in the standard text does Cattell.

Going back still further I had a look at the biologists and particularly at Darwin. He apparently never used it, but he came near to it in his definition of the struggle for existence. The concepts of stress and stressors were, of course, used in physics and engineering, and laws relating to these were formulated more than sixty years ago.

One finds the application of the word 'stress' to psychological and psychiatric problems coming into literature during, and particularly towards the end of, the last war. In Hunt's Symposium on Personality and Behaviour Disorders stress is given a little space in relation to the so-called 'frustration theory'. Here frustration, frustration tolerance and types of stress arousing frustration are defined.

The climate of opinion in which these ideas could flourish was no doubt developed in part from the work on experimental neurosis in animals, and from the recognition of physiological responses to physiological stressors. It was also developed, perhaps, from the great upheaval in personal living and the distresses which came to many people, both civil and military, which were the consequences of war. I mention this because the climate of opinion dependent on social upheaval is something we cannot resist. It occurs without our knowledge. It re-shapes, and gives new emphasis to, our ways of thinking about human behaviour, and these ways may or may not have enduring value. In this sense our preoccupation with stressors and stress as a valid aspect of the human scene may have been imposed upon us by the tyranny of words and circumstance. Do we yet know whether they will have survival value in the language of science? Differences between the nature of physical and biological systems and the environment which affects them are obviously important.

For a physical system the stressor is a physical stimulus measurable in physical terms, and the stress imposed on the system is a load defined in terms of the breaking point of the system. A metal structure, for example, must not be stressed to more than one-third of its ultimate breaking stress. A biological system, on the other hand, reacts actively to a harmful stress imposed upon it. At a simple level it re-organizes itself internally to maintain homeostasis. At a higher level the organism responds with behaviour the effect of which is to withdraw from the stimulus or situation stressing it. At a still higher level the organism responds with behaviour the effect of which is to abolish or neutralize the external stimulus or situation. Organisms with well-developed nervous systems have, in addition, the capacity to select the stimuli or situations to which they will respond and to ignore others, and moreover they possess a number of alternative behavioural responses to such situations. It seems that the higher the individual is in the evolutionary scale the greater is his capacity for selective reponse to situations and the greater are the number and variety of the responses themselves. At the level of insect life and in the early hours or weeks of bird and mammalian life the selectivity is of a small range and the number of responses very limited. The responses themselves have a stereotyped invariable quality. As the individual matures the responses increase in range and complexity, lose their stereotyped quality, and the selective capacity to choose stimuli and situations in the environment to which to respond becomes greatly increased.

This development must depend, of course, upon the twin processes of nervous system maturation and of learning. The first is conceived as largely an innate genetic process, the second as a process of experience of social interaction. At every moment of time each individual is under the influence of three sources of information which will determine future behaviour. Professor J. Z. Young suggested that these can be codified as, firstly, information provided by the world around, secondly information received from ancestors, the biogenetic equipment and, thirdly, information which each individual has acquired and stored during his lifetime. In physiological terms we know very little indeed about how this information is transmitted, stored or computed so that the appropriate adaptive response to any given situation is provided. What we can observe and what our speakers have described for us at this Conference are the variety of adaptive responses which are made and some of the circumstances in psycho-social terms which appear to be related.

The gap between psycho-social phenomena and physiological phenomena remains a wide one and it looks as if the bridge which must be built will remain a formidable undertaking. It is important, however, for us to know where it is feasible and proper to attempt to build such bridges.

It may be useful to draw attention briefly to the ways in which the majority of psychiatrists approach nearly every problem of neurotic illness. In the practice of psychiatry as soon as we attempt an understanding of a patient's problem or any psycho-therapeutic goal, we search both the immediate and past life of the patient for hypothetical stressors. We think we have identified them when we come upon circumstances which have generated unpleasant emotion in our patient. To be more precise, we try to find situations which we think should have generated unpleasant emotion, whether or not the patient admits that to the best of his conscious belief they have done so. If he does not we attempt to arouse and bring into his awareness the emotion which we infer he should have experienced. This is probably true of much of the routine psychiatric practice of today.

The emotions we are particularly interested in are, of course, anger, fear, resentment, longing, shame, guilt and a sense of loss or deprivation. If a patient has endured some experience which we, as sophisticated human beings, consider should have generated unpleasant emotion, yet the patient denies that it did so, we are all the more impressed by the observation and place greater significance upon it.

To a physiologist however, the observation that a patient is not experiencing, or has not experienced, unpleasant emotion might well lead to the conclusion that the event and the stimulus to emotional reactions which the event provided has been adapted to, and it might well lead him to the view that since all adaptations to the stressors are purposive and useful there is no more to be said about it.

The psycho-pathologist however, has for a long time claimed that certain adpatations, while purposive enough, may be harmful to the proper functioning of the organism as a whole. These adaptations are those which, while being adequate responses to an immediate situation, are inappropriate in the long run and leave the organism in a state of prolonged altered excitability, a state which in clinical terms we recognize as illness, the simplest expressions of which are called emotional tension, depression, withdrawl, limitation of activity and so on.

A closer analysis of the history of any patient shows that it is only rarely that any single event can be singled out as of primary etiological importance; or if any event can be singled out the criticism cannot be avoided that the choice has been made upon the personal bias of the observer, a bias dependent upon his psychiatric orientation and training. Rather it seems that the patient who has become ill has been involved in a matrix of factors which can be seen to be in some way related to the illness. Some of these factors can be described in terms of the patient's early experience and relationships, some in terms of recent experience and some in terms of the patient's in-born or acquired behavioural responses. But it is never easy and usually impossible to arrange these inter-related factors in any hierarchy or order of significance.

If this is so then the concept of a stressor as used in psychiatry with relevance to the development of illness cannot be used in an operational sense, for in this sense the stressor cannot be defined or measured. Every event is only a stressor by reason of the *meaning* which it has for the individual who experiences it. The stressor is, therefore, as much a function of the individual as it is of the environment and it owes its stressing quality as much to the personality of the individual stressed as to anything else.

Even if we have to abandon the idea of psychological stressors as specific and definable factors this Conference has provided us with some generalizations about the character of the environmental experience likely to facilitate or evoke stress in the individual. These have been described in terms of the social system in which the individual is constrained — the army is an example of such a social system — and in terms of stimuli which we can relate more easily to ways in which the central nervous system may respond.

The environmental situations are stressful or threatening if they bring about in the individual a high level of expectancy or anticipation, either that new stimuli will arrive which will prove inconsistent with previous adaptations or that the stimuli will be such as to spell disorganization or doom to the individual. Many speakers I think will agree that it is the *meaning* of experience that matters. All experiences involving disapproval, rejection, loss of dependent relationships, bereavement or deprivations constitute a threat. But all such psychological situations are, in Professor Selye's words 'conditional stressors', conditional in the sense that they depend upon the individual's state, that is his past experience. Professor Liddell goes further than this. He suggests that the degree of prolonged self-imposed restraint engendered in an animal called upon to make a continuous social adaptation is itself stressful, and in fact constitutes the greatest stress. The meaning of 'self-imposed restraint' might be taken, I suggest, as being equally a state of sustained anticipation.

Dr Hinde's studies bring us a little closer to the meaning of threats and the views he expresses are in line with clinical experience. He suggests that environmental situations induce stress if, (a) they simultaneously arouse in the individual tendencies to behave in incompatible ways — and (b) remove from the individual stimuli to which he is adapted and upon which his behaviour is dependent. These may be the positive and negative aspects of stressful environments, either that they contain too much, or that they contain too little. The former is associated with a stress state called conflict, the latter with a stress state called deprivation. These seem to be essentially different states.

It is important to distinguish between the state of stress and the consequence of stress. The consequences of stress may be adaptive and valuable to the individual and no doubt in most cases are so. Without stress there would be no learning and no individual achievement. On the other hand the consequences of stress may be maladaptive and neurotic illness, psychosomatic illness and deviant behaviour may result. These are new partial adaptations, partial in the sense of not being fully appropriate to the individual situation, and not fully rewarding or even not rewarding at all.

The state of stress may be an abstraction, but it can perhaps be regarded as the process of change during which a new adaptation is reached. We know very little about this process of change; we know far more about the consequences of it. Professor Lindemann describes it as a state of crisis which will lead to the adaptive or maladaptive response. It appears to be a state describable in clinical terms as one of high excitement, but with restricted motor activity.

How can we conceive this process as existing within the nervous system? One method is to think of it as a process of computation. Possible future events have to be predicted in the light of all past events and present circumstances. The individual has to draw upon all sources of information available to him. We have evidence that this state is associated with intense activity in the diencephalon producing on the one hand a state of cortical arousal and on the other greatly increased activity in the pituitary-adrenal system and in the sympathetic-adrenalin system. Different parts of these individual systems may be differentially activated in different states of stress, and about this Dr Hoagland had much to tell us. In the first place, as far as the output of the adrenocortical system to a stressful situation is concerned, the effects are inversely proportional to the success of the subject in performing the tasks set. The better an individual's performance and the greater, therefore, his adaptive capacity, the smaller the increase in 17-ketosteroids. It is possible also, that the pattern of steroid output is altered and this may be a function of that pre-test anxiety, of anticipatory tension. In older subjects who produced an increase in 17-ketosteroids to stress, when the pre-test scores were high the subjects did well in performance and put out less steroids during the tasks.

That the pattern of the adrenocortical response to stress can change, and that the quality of the stress in psychological terms is important, was vividly illustrated by observations made on the battle-stressed soldiers in Korea. Anxiety particularly would seem to alter the pattern. There is even better evidence that the pattern of hormone secretion from the adrenal medulla can be affected by different qualities in the stress situation, different qualities, that is, in terms of the psychological set. Vigorous and aggressive, outwardly-turned activity favours an increase in the noradrenalin component, whereas passive, tense, inwardly-turned activity — that is aggression directed on the self — favours an increase in the adrenalin component. From a knowledge of experimental neuro-physiology the former state can be identified with increased activity of the lateral hypothalamic areas, while the latter state is associated with increased activity in the posterior part of the hypothalamus. It may, therefore, be suggested that differentiation of the medullary response to different qualitative stress states occurs at the hypothalamic level. We have, as yet, no similar knowledge about the adrenocortical response. Here Professor Harris came in. It would be exciting to know whether the neuro-humoral agent carried in the portal system of the pituitary stalk is a single factor or whether at least two will be identified, as one might suspect.

I think the most important outcome of Professor Selye's evidence as far as the topic of this Conference is concerned is that the duration of stress determines the degree of its harmful effects. One would like to know how it is that the cat alone among many different species exposed to immobiliza-tion can survive. This evidence agrees well enough with that presented to us by Professor Liddell. It seems that protection of the body against injury or disease is carried out by a mechanism prolonged over-activity of which is dangerous to man and animal, and particularly to their psychological well-being.

This raises the question of the significance of these peripheral effects of the stress state for central nervous system activity. This is an area about which little is known, and this Conference has had little discussion upon it. The question is, to what extent are these systemic hormonal changes either harm-ful or facilitatory to the central process of resolution of the stress state to the forming of a new behavioural adaptation, whether for good or ill?

Dr Lacey made an important statement about this. He suggested that the autonomic nervous system is not just an atavistic mechanism which we should be better without, but is an important instrument of adaptation at all levels. It is not just an effector system, but the results of activity in it have important feed-back functions through the visceral afferent reflexes. These can operate at peripheral levels, as in the carotid sinus reflexes controlling cardiovascular activity, and also at central levels by feeding back stimuli to the mid-brain reticular system. From this it follows that the state of arousal or the antici-

atory state of the individual may be controlled by what happens in the
periphery. Since in differently named stress states the strain in the organism
differently distributed, different effects on the central arousal system can
be anticipated. Dr. Lacey considers that in children a constitutional organ
vulnerability is present. Later in life, however, he can range individuals on
a continuum, the extremes of which are from a very variable type of organ
response to a stereotyped fixed response. He emphasized that the stereotyped response was associated with psychosomatic illness. If this is so it raises
once again the question of the genetical determination of these hormonal
responses and the question of the extent to which they are modifiable by
learning. We know almost nothing about this.

This Conference might well direct its attention not so much to the effects
of stress, the clinical syndromes which in the case of the maladaptive response
may occur, but to the stress state itself, the process of reaching a new adaptation. We want to know what are the factors influencing this process. To
what extent can these factors only be described in psychological terms and
to what extent only in physiological terms? Is the degree or quality of the
physiological participation in this process important, and in what way?

I have already mentioned the visceral afferent feed-back system; activation
of the adrenal medulla is, of course, stimulatory to many peripheral systemic
processes, but on the contrary adrenalin would appear to have a central
depressant action at the diencephalic level. Dr Feldberg tells me that adrenalin
introduced into the third ventricle of the cat preparation produces an anaes-
thetic-like state and reduces spinal reflex excitability. On the other hand
there is some clinical evidence that ACTH and cortisone may have a positive
feed-back effect, increasing central excitability. Euphoric and even manic
states have been described in patients treated with these substances. Dr Hinde
has told us that he believes displacement behaviour in birds may be a consequence of widespread autonomic activity. It is very tempting to see this sort
of behaviour as the analogue of some deviant behaviour in man, particularly
of course obsessional tics and compulsions.

While the traditional positions of the experimental physiologist and the
psychoanalytic student of behaviour are drawing closer together there is
still a considerable gulf set between them, and I do not think we should ignore
it or pretend that it does not exist. The traditional position of the physiologist might be expressed somewhat as follows: stress can be inferred to
exist in the organism when certain chemical, neuronal and behavioural
responses to stimuli can be observed and measured. Our understanding of
stress will be complete when all these possible changes are known and
measurable. Moreover the factors which bring stress about can be identified
in the environment of the organism, and they in turn should ultimately be

ascertainable and measurable. Within this scheme therefore it is held th
stressors relevant to the problem of mental illness should exist and be capab
of identification and measurement.

By contrast, the traditional position of the psychoanalytically orient
student might be stated as follows: stress exists in the organism and may w
be measurable in chemical, neuronal or behavioural terms, but this state
brought about as a result of the organism's recognition of the meaning
environmental stimuli, the alleged stressor situation. The meaning whic
stimuli may have is determined by the state of the subject's psychologic
needs at the time and the extent to which these are threatened. Moreov
the meaning of stimuli is most related to the meaning which previous simil
stimuli acquired in the past. Again, this was determined by the way suc
stimuli related to the psychological needs at that time, and were reacted to

Since we cannot measure meanings either in the present or in the pa
psychological stressors can never be measured but only described. They ar
of course, always particular to the individual. There is a further idea i
psychoanalytical and in some though not all ethological thinking whic
we have heard very little about at this Conference. This is the idea that ther
is an energy of instinctual or innate origin in all living organisms whic
activates the variety of the individual's needs, and that this energy is onl
dissipated in a series of consummatory acts of behaviour operating in th
environment, that is to say inter-personal transactions. The prevention c
these consummatory acts either by internal inhibition or by absence c
suitable triggering or sign stimuli, to use the ethologists' phrase, or of 'lov
objects', to use the psychoanalysts' phrase, leads to damming up of thi
innate energy and to unpleasant emotional tension. Such an individual i
then under stress.

The conditions determining sensitivity to stress seem to be related to th
individual's experience during the period of his immaturity, that is to sa
during the period when the individual is most helpless and most dependen
upon the parents for survival, and we had a good account of the recent worl
done by Dr Anthony in this field. These early experiences may determin
the individual's future responses to the social environment, especially to th
objects with which to relate. But there must also be important constitutiona
and genetically determined factors.

The activity conceived as present during the stress process has many o
the characteristics we associate with memory functions. This activity persist
through sleep and through anaesthesia, is not abolished by concussion or by
a variety of cerebral insults, but can be reduced by some sedative and tranquillizing drugs and can occasionally be abolished by ECT or by leucotomy.
It can also be modified to some degree by change of scene, by modifying the

cial environment, particularly if this entails the removal of the patient's
rsonal contacts, the social environment to which he should be habituated
t is not. Clinical practice suggests that all these are temporary expedients;
mammals and certainly man must relate to a social environment. Isolation
no answer. Indeed one recalls here the work of those who have demon-
rated the mental disorganization of normal men isolated from sensory and
otor contact with the environment. Moreover action in some form reduces
nsion. This may be simple motor activity as in manual work, or highly
omplex pieces of organized behaviour such as the displacement activity of
irds or vicarious motor work and the use of verbalization in man which,
; we all know, is a good method of reducing tension and alleviating stress.

It is doubtful whether the state of stress as defined can be long sustained.
resumably it can be dissipated by rest when the individual is withdrawn
om the stressful situation. It can lead to exhaustion and inertia, or it can
ad to a new adaptation, successful or deviant. Professor Wolff has assured
s, however, that repeated states of stress or prolonged stress lead to inca-
acity, many diseased states and early death, and Professor Selye has thrown
uch light on the peripheral mechanisms that bring such events about.

One of the ideas, therefore, which has emerged from this Conference is
at any degree of prolongation of stress, any hold-up in the adaptive process
itself intrinsically harmful, not only to psychological health but also to
hysical health, and is potentially dangerous to life. It might be inferred that
maladaptive response such as a neurosis or a psychopathic act is better
om the point of view of survival than a prolongation of stress.

On therapeutic considerations only one thing remains. Sherrington, I
hink it was, suggested that the best adaptation was in motor activity, acting
ut, if you will. The next best adaptation is in symbolic motor activity, that
; verbalization, translated into psychiatric language as communication or
sychotherapy. The last and least successful adaptation is internalized motor
ctivity, that is fantasy work. It is to be noticed that the first two of these
equire for their functioning an environment in which to operate. As a
linician I have the personal conviction that in most cases it is the quality of
he social environment which determines whether successful adaptation to
sychological stress will occur.

GENERAL DISCUSSION (B)

Ralph Gerard

Neuropsychiatric Institute, University of Michigan

I have divided my points under the following headings: *unity, time-flow, experience and personality,* and *stress.* This will have the advantage, I hope, of making my remarks sound profound, whether they are nor not!

Unity

I was a little saddened at the reviving tendency to pit 'physiological' against 'psychiatric'. This dichotomy is an old and unfortunate one, and I prefer to approach these problems from the point of view of the behavioural scientist, which includes both the biological and the psychological approaches. May I use that term as an excuse to call to the attention of those not familiar with it the journal *Behavioural Science?* Most of those interested in this symposium would find it of interest and I especially note the issue of April 1958 devoted to a conference on 'Concepts of Biology'

One discussion here focused particularly on the problem of the meaning and measurability of psychological stresses. I have always liked the words 'coded' and 'uncoded'; but these are close to 'conditioned' or 'unconditioned' as applied to stresses. We all agree that meaning is important, that worry needs the co-operation of a worrier, but I do not think that the difference between biological and psychological stresses are of this character. In fact I do not think the differences are basic.

Let me indicate the reasons for that opinion. Organisms are coded biologically just as much as they are psychologically; they have become conditioned, if you will, to particular kinds of stimuli which then matter to that individual organism under the existing situation. This is true whether the conditioning was recent, or far in the distant past. In the one case, I remind you of the phenomenon of immunity, in which the individual experience may be very early; in the other case, I remind you of shifts in drug responsiveness and sensitivity depending on what doses have been given, when, and under what conditions. There can thus be vastly different responses to a given biological stimulus or stress or challenge. The existence of trigger points, evoking vigorous responses of the nervous system, and the irritation of central nervous system regions which produce changes in responsiveness that can endure for the life of the organism, indicate the importance of the past biologically as well as psychologically. Indeed, the whole essence of a higher level system is that this depends to a much greater extent than does a lower one on the particular accidents and vicissitudes of past experience which are borne along into the present.

That organisms have as much biological as psychological individuality is platitudinous, but I mention it since we paid little attention to it. One cannot transfer tissues, between species or even within species; there is difficulty until one gets to the individual himself. There is specificity in terms of patterns of metabolites and hormones, in the blood and urine of the individual body, comparable to the specificity of the individual or community nest. A social insect, getting into the wrong nest, will be set upon and often destroyed until it has acquired that particular nest smell. Such attributes of the individual do not remain constant even for that individual; they fluctuate from time to time with many conditions.

Another point is that the psychological meaning of a stimulus or stressor can in certain cases be identified physiologically or biologically. I remind you of those dramatic experiments in which the electrical response in the cochlear ganglion, to a sound of fixed intensity repeated at regular intervals, does not remain constant. If there is no reinforcement, if this is a neutral sound, it soon ceases to evoke any considerable potential. This is a physiological measure of boredom. Conversely, if the sound has significance to the organism — as the cry of a baby that the mother hears — a signal of food or punishment to come, it grows in magnitude. This is a feed-back control from the central nervous system, and under the jurisdiction, in part at least, of the reticular formation. But that is not the point; here is a physiological measure of changed psychological meanings.

The last point in this section, perhaps the most important one, is that, while it is perfectly true that individuality carries right down to the single organism, if there were nothing but complete individuality we would get nowhere scientifically. Biology would then remain forever a wonderful art but not lend itself to the powerful generalizations of science, which depend on eliminating the idiosyncratic specificities and finding the remaining common class residuals.

At the psychological as well as at the biological level, despite the great individual differences that occur, I think there remain far greater commonalities; the things we are able to experiment with in humans are those which can be reproduced from case to case despite individual variability. One is faced always with a plethora of information as one explores the environment. It is the cry of those who experiment in the psycho-social realm that it is easy to amass data which are impossible to handle. This is the problem of getting from the idiosyncratic attributes of the individual to the common properties of the class, and I submit that these are very rich even in the psychological area; generalizations are possible.

Time-flow

We have allowed ourselves to get into bad verbal habits in speaking of the past influencing the present, or the future influencing the present. The

TABLE 22

	Being	Behaving	Becoming
Society . .			
Group . .			
Individual .			
Organ . .			
Cell . . .			
Molecule . .			

past never influences the present; all that happens is that residual traces from the past are present at a given time. And the future never influences the present; all that happens is that certain expectations as to the future are present at a given time. To speak otherwise, I think, gets us into the kind of mellifluous sound made by philosophers who argue as to 'whether the present is exfoliated from the fullness of the past or sucked forward by the vacuity of the future'. The point, of course, is that the traces of the past must depend on some material carrier and this is true not only at the level of the individual but at that of the society.

Table 22 we use incessantly at our Institute. If one considers the several levels of organization of different systems — from molecule to cell, organ, ndividual, group or society — it appears that systems at all levels do have certain attributes which are homologous. Each horizontal level can be divided to form vertical columns which I have called, being addicted to alliteration, 'Being', 'Behaving', and 'Becoming': structure, organization, morphology, architecture; functioning, performing responding; and evolving, developing, the historical aspect. It is then possible to think up and down the columns and across the rows. The table is an extremely helpful intellectual hat rack, if you will, on which to place one's concepts; for they do fall into some unification.

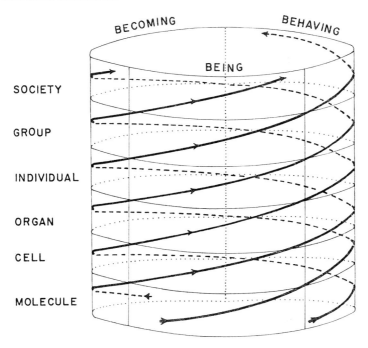

Fig. 9.—Relation between levels of organization (see text).

One hears the aphorism that structure is frozen function, and there is argument as to whether it is meaningful to divide these up. Yet in practice it turns out that it is. If one considers behaviour at any level it turns out that analysis of it involves the structure at the level below that. And to understand the structure, involves the history, or the 'becoming', at the next lower level; which, in turn, comes from the 'behaving' at the level below that. There is, thus, a series of ascending spirals which show mechanisms at these different levels. (Fig. 9.) They represent the relations of micro or analytic explanation.

10

'Being' is essentially a cross-section in the time axis. This is the system as it is now. Attention is focused on it in slices — what it would be like at this time cross-section or at another similar time cross-section. Properties which are congruous in both are called its structural organization — not the momentary position of the arm in space but the enduring fact that an arm is present in the organization. 'Behaving' and 'becoming' are longitudinal sections down the time axis; with 'behaving' representing changes which are reversible, ephemeral, in adjustment to the flow of environmental impingements; and 'becoming', the irreversible, secular, developmental changes, those states which, having been brought about, are essentially permanent. (They may not be completely permanent but endure for a different order of time magnitude from those of 'behaving'.)

At any given moment in time a system brings to the environment that it faces a certain pattern of heterogeneity which is determined by what has happened to it until then. The aspect of the environment most important to organisms has altered in the course of evolution. In the early stages, the main relation was to the physical environment. The primitive plant or animal had to solve mainly problems of sustenance; of food and water supply, protection against cold and heat and drying. Later, the main features of the environment that demanded attention were biological, the biotic factors; competitors, prey, invaders, and so on. At the stage of man, the social environment, the intra-specific, inter-personal relations, are the most important factors that challenge the individual organism.

Consideration of the sorts of outcomes that result from this interaction, of the system in the here-and-now with the environment it faces in the here-and-now, has occupied a large part of the attention of this group. We call the outcome good or bad, neurotic or healthy, depending on a value judgment which is perhaps not quite so distressful as it may sound. The same situation applies to the whole problem of biological evolution, in which the sequence of species shifts with time under the impact of the environment. We speak of adaptive or non-adaptive changes. Whether changes are ultimately good or bad certainly depends on the kind of environment in which the organism finds itself. There is no absolute normative bases for right of wrong, good or bad. The criterion is success or lack of success, in terms of the organism as it then is and the environment it then faces. Many behaviours which are neurotic in a man, in terms of his ability to face new environments, are highly adaptive in terms of his ability to get along well in a restricted environment to which he has adjusted. The same has been true in biological evolution.

There is always, in the evolution of the species as well as in the development or behaviour of the individual, or of the lower units, some kind of a goal. I am not sure that man sets his goal in any more meaningful sense than that life sets its goal in the course of evolution; but this is a philosophical question that, fortunately, we need not go into. There is always the double projection into the future, that Sir Geoffrey Vickers brought out in his opening remarks, the projections of the expected and the desired. The whole process of living is riding this double rail forward into the future and attempting by appropriate adjustments to bring the expected into coincidence with the desired. Living is essentially a continuous tracking performance at the mental or judgmental level, based on the best probability expectations that the organism can toss up from its experience.

Experience and Personality

We turn to the third item, experience and personality. It is a universal attribute of living things that they move over time from a state of greater to one of lesser totipotency. They sacrifice some of their potentialities and gain in exchange a greater skill in the specialized area that they have chosen. This is true for the differentiated cells of the multicellular organism as compared with the undifferentiated whole of the unicellular, a single jack-of-all-trades. Evolution produces specialized organisms and organs and cells. Specialization is no less the case for the development and enculturation of the human baby, who comes to us a particular language, plays a certain role, occupies a given status, and so on.

The particular attributes of the body or of the personality associated with it are, of course, the progressive bench marks of experience. From hereditary start to adult climax, as I have pointed out, progressive particularization is the norm. Which changes become irreversible is a matter of major importance and in general those experiences which are more prolonged or more repeated or more intense are more likely to leave irreversible changes. At the level of neural mechanisms, we have some definite ideas about what gives irreversible changes and fixed memories.

Besides these ubiquitous factors, there are in the history of the organism certain periods of high impressionability — of imprintability, if I am not violating the use of a technical word — and that these periods are certainly related to those of role transition, as at birth, separation, weaning, adolescence, marriage, and so on. At these times the fixation of experience is particularly vivid and effective; and I suspect it is at these times that most of our essentially ineradicable prejudices, our superego structures, are established. It may also be that at these times, as Dr Sutherland implied, one can look forward most hopefully to repatterning what has already been laid down. During such a soft-shell stage of the brain and psyche, not only can the new be introduced but also the old can be replaced.

10§

I would like to emphasize, however, that experience is essential for this fixing, imprinting, learning; without experience one remains an amorphous mass. It is like cement that has been mixed with water without being placed in a mould; it hardens, to be sure, but remains useless and without shape. Templets based on past experience are needed to guide future experience. These are real things in the brain and not entirely figures of speech. The damage resulting from a brief separation of the goat and its kid struck me as of this sort. At this critical time after birth, certain experiences were essential to establish neural patterns critical to the normal interaction and further development of both those individuals. If the patterns were not then moulded, there was no later possibility of establishing them; the behaviours fixed were of the wrong type. From then on it was not lack of maternal care or of any other single item, it was rather a matter of a bad interaction between two organisms, and the normal one could never be re-established.

There has been other experimental work in this field. Baby chimpanzees raised in complete darkness for a few months from birth never learn to use pattern vision. Nothing has been done to their eyes or brain but they can not learn to see. The same is true of humans who lacked pattern vision in childhood. Later, removing an opaque lens or transplanting a clear cornea may provide a good optical instrument, yet it takes the most painful education to enable such persons to distinguish a square from a circle visually, however perfectly they may discriminate by touch.

Even more dramatic, perhaps, are experiments in which one occipital lobe of a chimpanzee was removed at a certain time and the other two weeks later. If, during the two-week interval, the animal is not allowed any visual experience it becomes functionally blind so far as pattern discrimination is concerned. If allowed visual experience in that two weeks the animal's vision remains all right. Somehow or other, the existing templet in one occipital lobe serves to lay down a new templet elsewhere in the brain.

I might now point out that these changes depend on the actual passage of nerve impulses along nerve fibres and across nerve synapses, probably involving rather considerable reverberation and repetitive activity. Without this kind of experience one gets no fulfilment, no development. Shall we call all of this experience 'stress' or not? I am reminded of a tombstone verse in the Spooner authology.

'Here lie the remains of Mary Hyde,
'For her life held no terrors;
'A virgin born, a virgin died,
'No hits, no runs, no errors.'

Stress

Last, I move on to the problem of stress and shall deal entirely with psychological stress. Our concern is both with input into the central nervous system and output from the central nervous system. Much too much information is available at the psycho-social level; the problem faced in identifying and quantifying important psycho-social stresses is not lack of knowledge, but rather surfeit of information and lack of discrimination regarding it. We must learn which are the important variables that must be retained and which items can safely be thrown away. Much of the work reported here during these several days was directed to this first problem: What is a good variable? A good variable is one for which an adequate degree of co-variation can be demonstrated between the sociopsychological situation imposed upon the organism and a response, either behavioural or somatic. With such co-variation one has a stimulus situation that can be manipulated; the next thing is to quantify it, and after that to find the mechanisms which communicate meaning to the subject.

The output to the body side, from such a stress, is the physiology of the autonomic and endocrine systems. As you have all become acutely aware, this is far enough advanced so that the problems are losing general interest and belong largely to specialists. The questions are of details: How does this work; how does that work? The broad picture is now quite clear: there are outflows, from the diencephalon primarily but not exclusively; through the orthosympathetic system to the adrenal medulla; through the hypothalamic portal system to the pituitary and secondarily the adrenal cortex; through the parasympathetic system to the pancreas; through various of these routes to the liver, to other organs, and to the central nervous system itself.

One question which has perhaps been shirked a bit is whether these physiological responses occur together or separately. Are they all a measure of the same thing or not? The evidence is becoming overwhelming that they are not. It is quite true that with various stresses there will be changes in the nervous system as well as in the thymus, adrenal and gut; but whether they will run parallel or not and the extent of the variation with different stresses can only be established by the painful and prolonged process of examining each situation in its own right.

If we accept the term 'stressor' at the biological level, then I like the word 'challenge' or 'crisis' at the psychological level; if we take 'stress' at the biological level, to me the equivalent at the psychological level is 'tension' or 'anxiety'.

I find myself negative to the suggestion that there is a certain amount of adaptation capacity put into an organism, and that this is drawn upon with each stress until finally the pot is empty and the organism dies. Such a picture is certainly not congenial to a physiologist, who thinks of dynamic states and the balance between rates of formation and rates of destruction. There is no given total amount of capacity but the balance can be reduced dynamically for any given time, and sometimes to a dangerous degree. As the last task, I shall attempt the transliteration, asked for by several people, from the psycho-social to the neurophysiological. I have here the manuscript of a lecture I gave recently at the New York Academy of Medicine (Gerard, 1958) and shall save time by reading a portion of it.

'To me anxiety is largely connected with frustrated drives, especially under conditions under which the response is turned in. Anxiety is shown in dreams which involve a continuous activity of the brain due to unresolved or unassimilated recent experience. Anxiety is particularly associated with unfinished business, with events to come even more than events from the past. Anxiety is common when some important decision is to be made, when waiting for a particularly important message, as a 'phone call or letter; time then becomes interminable, the stress gets worse and worse as delay extends, and a predisposed person can go into a true anxiety panic. Really nothing whatever is happening; there is just maintained uncertainty. A person has the same kind of anxiety when the decision is not an external but an internal one, when faced with an important choice, when deciding whether to do this or that; with any important, unsolved problem a severe anxiety state can build up. With some unfinished business an individual is not at ease, not relaxed and such an unsettled state can last for years.

'Great creative scientists and artists have reported such unresolved problems gnawing at them for prolonged periods until the solution finally clicked and brought great relief. The same phenomenon occurs in the learning child. There is tension while some new experience or new concept remains unassimilated. Then with comprehension come real joy and excitement and release as the child says, "Oh, that's what it is, now I understand".

'Still another basis for anxiety is what I have called the unbalanced emotional evasion. If one person has wronged another, the latter either forgets it or builds up a sense of injury and tension and the resolve to get even some day. Finally, in one way or another this emotional balance is squared and the accounts are settled and the tension is discharged, even though the original damage to the settler is not thereby resolved. In its primitive form this reaction is seen in the child who, having stumbled on a rock, gives it a vigorous kick. This action somehow squares the emotional account, even though adding a new insult.

'Now the mechanisms: in the great majority of cases when a single nerve impulse comes to a synapse it does not succeed in exciting the neuron beyond, it dies out. Nonetheless, if several messengers in the same fibre or messengers in several fibres near each other focus upon the post-synaptic neuron, within a short time and a narrow space excitation builds up; they add or summate. Hence, whereas one impulse will not cause the post-synaptic neuron to discharge, repeated impulses will summate and discharge it.

'Summation is, therefore, the first phenomenon in the transmission of an impulse from neuron to neuron; messages come in but may not get through to a particular path. Yet, if they continue to come in for a while, they do get through. Additional neurons are engaged and become part of the active system. This is one step.

'Suppose now that more and more messages reach the second neuron. Again summation may occur and after a while a third neuron will become active. There results a progressive spread of messages to more and more active neurons. This is the phenomenon of irradiation, and a continued flow of nerve messages can lead to widespread activation.

'This is the second step, and leads to a third one. Most pathways do not simply start with the neuron at one end and continue through a simple chain to the other. Only in the simplest reflex does the message follow such a route. In most cases some neurons can act, backed with others, to produce loops and the message may get into one, reach a second and third, et cetera, and find itself back where it started, and ready to go again around the same path. Actually the loops may be complicated, intricate, three-dimensional chains or assemblies of neurons, and impulses can reverberate for some time. First with summation, then with irradiation and then with reverberation and loop systems a continued stimulus may set up impulses that keep going over the same pathway like a merry-go-round for very considerable periods. Finally, if they go around often enough they leave some kind of irreversible trace or change in the nervous system and enduring memory; the organism has learnt from experience.

'We were able to show this decisively by experiments in which electric shocks were applied to hamsters so as to stun their brains. If the animals ran a maze and received a shock an hour later they remembered what they had learned, but if they received the shock a few minutes later they retained nothing. Time had to elapse after the actual experience during which fixation went on in the nervous system.

'Most of the problems presented by the environment in which the organism has to exist and maintain itself are repetitive and familiar, and the solutions are similarly routine. Most of the events in the nervous system, therefore, are not new; in fact, most solutions have been built in during the evolution of the race. Reflex paths are operative in the new-born nervous system, and the responses handled disturbing situations by pulling away from the pain-producing object, inducing winking the eye, and a myriad other inborn automatic reflexes.

'Furthermore, something learned can also become reflex, automatic and unconscious. As long as the available solution achieved by racial or individual habit resolves the problem, eliminates the stimulus, that response is sufficient, and in the overwhelming number of instances the action goes on quite unconsciously. You have all experienced this, perhaps, as I have: you have started to change a shirt for dinner and the first thing you know you have found yourself undressed and in bed! When one's mind is on something else when initiating the chain of habitual acts the whole sequence may be executed without the least awareness of it.

'But when the routine behaviour does not suffice to eliminate the disturbances, answer the question, resolve the issue, when there is unfinished business, then, of course, the stimulus continues. Impulses still pour into the nervous system since the automatic response was ineffective and a new kind of behaviour, creative or innovative behaviour, is called for. New paths through the nervous system are required, and the mechanisms already considered produce them. With the stimulus continuing, extra nerve impulses pour into the brain, produce summation at the regular synapses, and so are able to irradiate to new neurons and then set up reverberation activity in new loops of the total neuron network. Similarly, volume spread may occur in hypersynchronization and develop for those who want to think about it. With sufficiently continued reverberation or synchronism, permanent trace is left behind and experience is fixed. This is involved in memory, probably also in repression and even in perception. When these new neuron fixations or behavioural habits are inappropriate, a neurosis is the result. When the disturbance is sufficiently great, additional emergency mechanisms come into play, irradiation seems to spread from the newer axis or from the new brain into the old brain by hypothalamus and reticular alerting system and the adrenal hormones from the reticular formation, generalized nerve impulses barrage the cerebrum and so reinforce the messages coming from the outside world. Messages from the hypothalamus lead to the release of adrenalin, which lowers the threshold of cerebral neurons.

'The combination of more stimuli arriving with fewer stimuli required to excite necessarily results in a more rapid and extensive irradiation of excitation in the brain. As more neurons are engaged anxiety appears. You can produce anxiety with epinephrine; with mild anxiety and a moderate increase in active neurons there is, as one might expect, a general improvement in performance; with medium anxiety and a considerable fraction of the available neurons engaged performance becomes more rigid, with less exploration of alternative behaviours. Again this is what would be expected from the decreased reserve of uncommitted neurons.

'Finally, with severe anxiety most of the neuron reserve is committed to existing assemblies and to carrying unreproductive reverberating messages, and performance deteriorates and even collapses.

'With no cell reserves remaining, which may be a physiological translation of loss of psychic energy, innovative behaviour is no longer possible and actions again become stereotyped but are now non-adaptive or neurotic. Ordinarily, the innovative behaviour accompanied by only tolerable anxiety does solve the problem or finish the business, and the type of closure is attained. The surging patterns of activity cease in the brain and unless the episode was sufficiently intense and prolonged to produce a permanent fixation, the whole is wiped out. A good example is the way one holds a telephone number in memory after finding it in the book but forgets it immediately after the dialling is completed.

'However, when the stimulation has been excessive or the neuron thresholds have been too low, than some of the activity set up may endure long after the disturbance has disappeared. Then an abnormal level of activity rate may remain as a chronic state and produce mental illness. This is probably involved in neurosis, as in a chronic anxiety state due to excessive stimulation, and if some present views regarding schizophrenia gain support, such as the presence of excessive amounts of adrenalin in the oxidation products or of other endogenous substances, then the over-active state of this disease might be interpreted in terms of the lower neuron thresholds producing the chronic disturbance.

'We are already at or even beyond the limits of safe interpretation from biological conditions to psychological performance and it is time to close. We might tend to conclude, from the way in which this story has been developed, that the ideal state is one of minimal disturbance in adjustment, but this would be a false conclusion. A balance of stimulation and the resolution of stimulation is needed, both during development and in maturity. Too little environmental disturbance leads not to Nirvana but rather to a vegetable-like existence. Brief periods of minimal sensory stimulation may lead to psychosis. Too much harassment and stress from the outside world, conversely, leads to an unhappy and ineffectual life. Man functions best when a moderate number of neurons is active and when there remains a reasonable number in reserve. The extremes of not a brain cell working on the one side, and of all brain cells engaged in useless reverberating activity on the other are not desirable states. Fortunately, man has additional built-in mechanisms that help him seek a proper level of brain activity; after a bout of activity fatigue and sleep set in. Indeed, the function of sleep may be just to interfere with on-going reverberations that otherwise would become too fixed and permanent. With advancing age and the reduced reserve of usable neurons, there is a general slowing and an attendant decrease in environmental demands. Man has found in nature drugs to depress and stimulate his nervous system, and he early learnt to improve upon what was at hand. Every group of civilized men has used the depressants available to it, opium, hashish, marihuana, alcohol, but even more widely and enthusiastically used are the stimulants, tea, coffee, maté, cocoa. Man seeks to find and meet the challenge of a dynamic existence. As the fires cool, as passion is spent, he speaks with Swinburne:

"From too much love of living,
From hope and fear set free,
We thank with brief thanksgiving
Whatever gods may be
That no man lives forever,
That dead men rise up never;
That even the weariest river
Winds somewhere safe to sea."

But while in the full surge of maturity man presses against the frontier of life, and speaks with Louis Untermeyer:

"From compromise and things half done
Keep me, with stern and stubborn pride;
And when at last the fight is won,
God keep me still unsatisfied." '

BIBLIOGRAPHY

Albeaux-Fernet, M., Bugard, P. and Romani, J. D. (1957) Excretion of urinary corticoids in conditions of chronic asthenia. *J. clin. Endocrin.* **17**, 519–533.

Andrew, R. J. (1956a) Intention movements of flight in certain passerines, and their use in systematics. *Behaviour*, **10**, 179–204.

Andrew, R. J. (1956b) Some remarks on behaviour in conflict situations, with special reference to *Emberiza* spp. *Brit. J. Anim. Behav.* **4**, 41–45.

Anthony, E. J. (1957) An experimental approach to the psychopathology of childhood: encopresis. *Brit. J. med. Psychol.* **30**, 146–175.

Anthony, E. J. (1959) An experimental approach to the psychopathology of childhood: sleep disturbances. *Brit. J. med. Psychol.* **32**, 19–37.

Barnett, S. A. (1958) Physiological effects of 'Social Stress' in wild rats. 1. The adrenal cortex. *J. psychosom. Res.* **3**, 1–11.

Bowlby, J. (1958) The nature of the child's tie to his mother. *Int. J. Psycho-Anal.* **39**, 5—350–373.

Christian, J. J. (1950) The adreno-pituitary system and population cycles in mammals. *J. Mammal.* **31**, 247–259.

Clarke, J. R. (1953) The effect of fighting on the adrenals, thymus and spleen of the vole (*Microtus agrestis*). *J. Endocrin.* **9**, 114–126.

Curle, A. (1947–48) Transitional communities and social reconnection: A follow-up study of the civil resettlement of British prisoners of war. Part. I. *Hum. Relat.* **1**, 42–68.

Curle, A. and Trist, E. L. (1947–48) Transititional communities and social reconnection: A follow-up study of the civil resettlement of British prisoners of war. Part II. *Hum. Relat.* **1**, 240–288.

Davis, D. Russell (1957) *An Introduction to Psychopathology.* London.

Dicks, H. V. (1953) Clinical studies in marriage and the family: a symposium on methods. *Brit. J. med. Psychol.* **26**, 181–196

Dickson, D. E. (1936) The Morbid Miner. *Edinb. med. J.* N.S. **43**, 696–705.

Dittes, J. E. (1957) Galvanic skin response as a measure of patient's reaction to therapist's permissiveness. *J. abnorm. soc. Psychol.* **55**, 295–303.

Elmadjian, F., Hope, J. M. and Lamson, E. T. (1957) Excretion of epinephrine and norepinephrine in various emotional states. *J. clin. Endocrin.* **17**, 608–620.

ELMADJIAN, F., HOPE, J. M. and LAMSON, E. T. (1958) Excretion of epinephrine and norepinephrine under stress. *Recent Progr. Hormone Res.* **14**, 513–553.

VON EULER, U. S. and HELLNER, S. (1951) Excretion of noradrenaline, adrenaline and hydroxytyramine in urine. *Acta physiol. scand.* **22**, 161–167.

FUNKENSTEIN, D. H., KING, S. H., DROLETTES, M. E. (1957) *Mastery of Stress* Cambridge, Mass.

FURER, M. and HARDY, J. D. (1950) The reaction to pain as determined by the galvanic skin response. *Ass. Res. nerv. Ment. Dis. Proc.* **29**, 72–89.

GADDUM, J. H. and LEMBECK, F. (1949) The assay of substances from the adrenal medulla. *Brit. J. Pharmacol.* **4**, 401–408.

GERARD, R. W. (1957) In 'Integrating the Approaches to Mental Disease'. Ed. Kruse, H. D. London.

GRINDLEY, G. C. (1929–30) Experiments on the influence of the amount of reward on learning in young chickens. *Brit. J. Psychol.* **20**, 173–180.

HALLIDAY, J. L. (1949 reprint) 1st edition 1948. *Psychosocial Medicine: A Study of the Sick Society.* London.

HERXHEIMER, H. (1951) Induced asthma in man. *Lancet*, **I**, 1337–1341.

HIGGIN, G. W. (1960) Studies in work organization at the coal face I. *Hum. Relat.* **13**, no. 1.

HILL, J. M. M. and TRIST, E. L. (1953) A consideration of industrial accidents as a means of withdrawal from the work situation. *Hum. Relat.* **6**, no. 4, 357–380.

HILL, J. M. M. and TRIST, E. L. (1955) Changes in accidents and other absences with length of service. *Hum. Relat.* **8**, no. 2, 121–152.

HILL, S. R., GOETZ, F. C., FOX, H. M., MURAWSKI, B. J., KRAKAUER, L. J., REIFENSTEIN, R. W., GRAY, S. J., REDDY, W. J., HEDBERG, S. E., ST. MARC, J. R. and THORN, G. W. (1956) Studies on adrenocortical and psychological response to stress in man. *Arch. intern. Med.* **97**, 269–298.

HINDE, R. A. (1956) The nest building behaviour of domesticated canaries. *Proc. zool. Soc. Lond.* **131**, 1–48.

HINDE, R. A. and TINBERGEN, N. (1958) *The comparative study of species-specific behaviour.* In *Behaviour and Evolution*, ed. A. Roe and G. C. Simpson. Yale University Press.

HOAGLAND, H., ELMADJIAN, F. and PINCUS, G. (1946) Stressful psychomotor performance and adrenal cortical function as indicated by the lymphocyte response. *J. clin. Endocrin.* **6**, 301–311.

HOAGLAND, H., PINCUS, G., ELMADJIAN, F., ROMANOFF, L., FREEMAN, H., HOPE, J., BALLAN, J., BERKELEY, A. and CARLO, J. (1953) Study of adrenocortical physiology in normal and schizophrenic men. *Arch. Neurol. Psychiat. (Chicago)*, **69**, 470–485.

HOAGLAND, H., BERGEN, J. R., BLOCH, E., ELMADJIAN, F. and GIBREE, N. R. (1955–56) Adrenal stress responses in normal man. *J. appl. Physiol.* **8**, 149–154.

HOLZAPFEL, M. (1939) Uber Bewegungsstereotypien bei gehaltenen Säugern. *Z. Tierpsychol.* **2**, 46–72.

IERSEL, J. J. A. VAN and BOL, A. C. (1958) Preening of two tern species. A study of displacement. *Behaviour*, **13**, 1–88.

JONES, H. E. (1935) The galvanic skin reflex as related to overt emotional expression. *Amer. J. Psychol.* **47**, 241–251.

KANTER, V. B. and SANDLER, J. (1955) Studies in psychopathology using a self-assessment inventory: Anxiety, functional dyspepsia and duodenal ulcer: an investigation. *Brit. J. med. Psychol.* **28**, 157–166.

KASS, E. H., HECHTER, O., MACCHI, I. A. and MOU, T. W. (1954) Changes in patterns of secretion of corticosteroids in rabbits after prolonged treatment with ACTH. *Proc. Soc. exp. Biol. (N.Y.)* **85**, 583–587.

KLEITMAN, N. (1939) *Sleep and Wakefulness*. Chicago.

LINDEMANN, E. (1944) Symptomatology and management of acute grief. *Amer. J. Psychiat.* **101**, 141–148.

LINDEMANN, E. (1950) in 'Life Stress and Bodily Disease'. Modifications in the course of ulcerative colitis in relationship to changes in life situations and reaction patterns. *Ass. Res. nerv. Dis. Proc.* **29**, 706–723.

LINDEMANN, E. (1957) in 'Understanding Your Patient,' Problems related to grandparents. Ed. S. Liebman, pp. 147–158. Philadelphia, Lippincott, J. B.

MALAMUD, W., HOPE, J. M. and ELMADJIAN, F. (1951) Objective evaluation of therapeutic procedures in mental diseases. *Boston Medical Quarterly* **2**, 1, 1.

MANACÉINE, M. DE (1897) *Sleep: its Physiology, Pathology, Hygiene and Psychology* London.

MASSERMAN, J. H. (1943) *Behaviour and Neurosis*. Chicago.

MORRIS, D. (1952) Homosexuality in the ten-spined stickleback. *Behaviour*, **4**, 233–261.

MORRIS, D. (1956) The feather postures of birds and the problem of the origin of social signals. *Behaviour*, **9**, 75–113.

MOYNIHAN, M. (1955) Some aspects of reproductive behaviour in the black-headed gull (*Larus ridibundus*) and related species. *Behaviour, Suppl. No. 4*, 1–201.

PACE, N., SCHAFFER, F. L., ELMADJIAN, F., MINARD, D., DAVIS, S. W., KILBUCK, J. H., WALKER, E. L., JOHNSTON, M. E., ZILINSKY, A., GERARD, R. W., FORSHAM, P. H. and TAYLOR, J. G. (1956) Physiological Studies on Infantrymen in Combat. Berkeley, in: California University— Publications in Physiology, 10, no. 1, pp. 1–48.

PINCUS, G. and HOAGLAND, H. (1943) Steroid excretion and the stress of flying. J. Aviat. Med. 14, 173–193.

RABER, H. (1948) Analyse des Balzverhaltens eines domestizierten Truthahns. Behaviour, I, 237–266.

REES, L. (1953) Psychosomatic aspects of the premenstrual syndrome. J. ment. Sci. 99, 62–73.

REES, L. (1956) J. psychosom. Res. I, 98.

REES, L. (1958) in Psychoendocrinology, Ed. Reiss. New York, Grune & Stratton.

RICE, A. K. (1958) Productivity and Social Organization: The Ahmedabad Experiment. London.

SANDLER, J. (1954) The development and construction of the Inventory. Brit. J. med. Psychol. 27, 3, p. 142.

SANDLER, J. and POLLOCK, A. B. (1954A) Some neurotic gastro-intestinal symptoms: Functional dyspepsia in men. Brit. J. med. Psychol. 27, 3, p. 146.

SANDLER, J. and POLLOCK, A. B. (1954B) Some neurotic gastro-intestinal symptoms: Functional dyspepsia in women. Brit. J. med. Psychol. 27, 4, p. 235.

SELYE, H. and CO-WORKERS (1950–55/6) Stress: Annual Reports on Stress, volumes 1–5. Montreal.

SELYE, H. (1952) The Story of the Adaptation Syndrome. Montreal.

SELYE, H. (1957) The Stress of Life. London: Longmans.

SELYE, H. (1958) The Chemical Prevention of Cardiac Necroses. New York.

SHEFFIELD, F. D., WULFF, J. J. and BACKER, R. (1951) Reward value of copulation without sex drive reduction. J. comp. physiol. Psychol. 44, 3–8.

SHERMAN, M. and JOST, H. (1945) Quantification of psychophysiological measures. Psychosom. Med. 7, 215–219.

SPIEGEL, J. P. (1959) in 'Individual aud Familial Dynamics.' Some cultural aspects of transference and counter-transference. Ed. Masserman, J. H. pp. 161–182. Grune & Stratton Inc.

STANTON, A. H. and SCHWARTZ, M. S. (1954) The Mental Hospital: a Study of Institutional Participation in Psychiatric Illness and Treatment. London.

TINBERGEN, N. (1952) Derived activities; their causation, biological significance, origin and emancipation during evolution. *Quart. Rev. Biol.* **27**, 1–32.

TINBERGEN, N. (1953) *The Herring Gull's World.* London.

TRIST, E. L. and BAMFORTH, K. W. (1951) Some Social and psychological consequences of the Longwall method of coal-getting. *Hum. Relat.* **4**, 3–38.

TRIST, E. L. and MURRAY, H. (1958) *Work organization at the coal face: A comparative study of mining systems.* London: Tavistock Institute of Human Relations, Document 506.

TRIST, E. L. and SOFER, C. (1959) *Explorations in Group Relations.* Leicester University Press.

VENNING, E. H. and DYRENFURTH, I. (1956) Effect of stress upon excretion of aldosterone. (Abstract) *J. clin. Endocrin.* **16**, 961.

WILSON, A. T. M. and TRIST, E. L. (1953) *The Bolsover system of continuous mining.* London: Tavistock Institute of Human Relations, Document 290.

INDEX